The Book of
GEESE

a Complete Guide
to Raising the Home Flock

The Book of
GEESE

a Complete Guide
to Raising the Home Flock

Dave Holderread
Illustrated by Millie Holderread

THE HEN HOUSE
P.O. Box 492
Corvallis, Oregon 97330

Library of Congress Catalog Card Number: 80-84195
International Standard Book Number: 0-931342-02-3

Typesetting by Corvallis Gazette-Times
Printing by Herald Press, Scottdale, Pennsylvania
Manuscript edited by Wanita Miller
Photographs: Page 120 by Marilyn Holderread
All other photographs by Dave and Millie Holderread

Dedicated to Dad . . .
who has shared with me
his appreciation and knowledge of the soil
and the plants and animals it sustains . . .

Contents

TABLES

Foreword

The Book of Geese, like its companion volume *The Home Duck Flock*, promises to be a valuable reference for waterfowl raisers at all production levels. It is the first full-length English language book devoted solely to geese. Although basic enough for the hobbyist, it is comprehensive enough for commercial producers and scientists as well. Dave's straightforward and complete coverage of these unheralded but extremely versatile fowl is most timely, especially now that people are showing genuine concern for the environment and raising food animals on a minimum of grain.

One of the unique and valuable characteristics of geese is their ability to utilize large quantities of forage. Recent research at Oregon State University has confirmed that geese can digest 15 to 20 percent of the fiber in their diet, compared to less than 5 percent in other species of poultry. As energy and meat prices continue to rise, what is more appropriate than a fowl capable of replacing herbicides by weeding crops, flourishing in wet, swampy areas not used by other grazing animals, and consuming mostly grass and other vegetation rather than grains and soybean meal, while producing excellent meat and the highest quality insulation for clothing and bedding.

Because of their convenient size and smaller per head investment compared to other domestic grazing animals, geese show great potential not only for small raisers in the U.S., but also for people in developing countries by providing more low-cost protein in the diet. Geese are also easier to care for and more disease resistant than most other poultry. No doubt their time is finally here. I, for one, think it is long overdue.

Al Hollister
Department of Poultry Science
Oregon State University
Corvallis, Oregon

Acknowledgments

The Book of Geese was made possible because many people shared their time, knowledge and resources. While it is not feasible to mention everyone who helped in this project, the following persons deserve a special word of thanks — G.H. Arscott, head of Poultry Science Department, Oregon State University; Frank Braman, poultry judge and lifelong waterfowl breeder; Bud Butcher, waterfowl and game bird breeder; Fred Cervinka, Heart of Missouri Hatchery; Don Helfer, DVM, Associate Professor Veterinary Medicine, Oregon State University; Al Hollister, Oregon State University Poultry Department; Lester Lind, West Virginian miller; Wanita Miller, our efficient editor and typist; Curtis Oakes, lifelong waterfowl breeder and APA judge; Larry and Cathy Passmore, Oregonian woodworking artists; Andrea Peterson, enthusiastic young goosekeeper; Darrell Sheraw, waterfowl breeder and APA judge; Tim and Doretta Schrock, Montana State University; Cathy Weeder, Fruit's Weeder Geese; and Fred and Marge Wright, Willow Hill Farm and Hatchery.

Introduction

Geese are considered one of the oldest forms of poultry, apparently having been domesticated at least 3,000 years ago. However, there has not been a book available dealing solely with these useful birds. The incentive for preparing *The Book of Geese* was to provide a manual on the care and breeding of domestic geese that would be comprehensive in scope, yet easily understood. Through the text and illustrations, we've tried to show the conditions under which these waterfowl are a practical addition to the homestead or farm, and how to manage them for the greatest degree of efficiency and enjoyment.

We are committed to home food production and small, diversified family farms. It is our feeling that it's good for people to be actively involved in the production of at least some of their own food. Most of us find that homegrown or locally produced foods are tastier. In many instances, such foods are more nutritious since they are fresher and do not need to be preserved with foreign chemicals during transportation and long storage periods. Homegrown foods or those acquired locally can also save natural resources due to reduced packaging and cross-country transportation. Of greatest importance on a global scale, relying on locally grown foods can help free land for the raising of staple foods in countries that are unable to feed their people because prime agricultural land is being exploited by multinational corporations who raise luxury export crops for the wealthier people of the world.

Although geese are certainly not "the answer" to the world hunger problem, they do fill an important niche in an environmentally sound scheme of food production. These big birds are the only true grazers in the poultry clan and they can utilize large quantities of forage that often goes unused. They are especially adept at gleaning grasses from hard-to-reach places — such as fence rows, ditches, and marshy areas — where larger livestock may not be practical. Plus, geese can be used as lawn mowers and weeders, and "companion planted" among orchard trees and cane berries. And not to be overlooked are their feathers that are so useful in winterizing our clothing and bedding.

In laying the ground work for *The Book of Geese*, sixty veteran poultry breeders, judges and hatchery operators from across North America were corresponded with or interviewed. Additionally, to insure accuracy and complete coverage, the manuscript was reviewed and critiqued by homesteaders, knowledgeable waterfowl breeders, commercial hatchery operators and specialists in avian diseases and nutrition.

The material presented in a number of the tables and in various sections of the text was obtained from work conducted through the vocational poultry program at Academia Menonita Betania, near Aibonito, Puerto Rico. The studies carried out in that program were designed to compare the productivity and practical qualities of all major poultry species under varied conditions.

While care has been taken to provide reliable and thorough information, please keep in mind that this handbook is meant to be used as a guide, not a golden rule. In the raising and breeding of livestock, there are such numerous variables involved that they cannot all be taken into account in a book. Geese can and often do respond differently than the norm, depending on factors such as environment, temperament of their caretaker and peculiar breed or strain characteristics. So don't be afraid to experiment and find which methods work best in your situation, with your birds.

Most geese are kept for their useful qualities. But we hope your days are not so busy that you can't also enjoy the graceful beauty and amusing antics that these stately birds provide if you'll just take time to watch. Happy goose raising!

Dave & Millie Holderread

CHAPTER 1

Why Geese?

If you and I could step back in time, we'd discover that small goose flocks were common on North American farms and homesteads through the first quarter of the twentieth century. These big birds were indispensible for many self-sufficient country folk. Geese supplied nutritious meat, huge eggs, rich fat for baking and flavoring, insulating down and feathers for bedding and winter clothing, and strong voices that greeted visitors or sounded the alarm when predators trespassed onto the homeplace.

And now, after nearly fifty years of decline, the popularity of the home goose flock is rebounding. As growing numbers of people return to gardening and small scale livestock production, we are discovering that geese are as useful today as they were in our grandparents' time.

ECONOMICAL

In areas where green grass is available during a good portion of the year, geese can be raised on less grain or concentrated feed than any other domestic fowl, with the possible exception of guinea fowl. Along with being great foragers, geese require little or no housing in most climates, and, if protected from predators and given reasonably good care, they have an extremely low mortality rate.

TABLE 1   GENERAL COMPARISON OF POULTRY

Bird	Raisability	Disease Resistance	Special Adaptations
Coturnix Quail	Good	Good	Egg and meat production in extremely limited space.
Guinea Fowl	Fair-Good	Excellent	Gamy-flavored meat; insect control; alarm. Thrive in hot climates.
Pigeons	Good	Good	Message carriers; meat production in limited space. Quiet.
Chickens	Fair-Good	Fair-Good	Eggs; meat; natural mothers. Adapt to cages, houses or range.
Turkeys	Poor-Fair	Fair-Good	Heavy meat production.
Ducks	Excellent	Excellent	Eggs; meat; feathers; insect, snail, slug, aquatic plant control. Cold, wet climates.
Geese	Excellent	Excellent	Meat; feathers; lawn mowers; "watch-dogs"; aquatic plant control. Cold, wet climates.

HARDY AND EASILY RAISED

One of the most attractive features of geese is their durability and ease of care. Along with ducks, they seem to be the most resistant of all poultry to disease, parasites and cold or wet weather. While chickens and turkeys normally need to be treated regularly for lice, mites, worms, coccidiosis and, in many localities, vaccinated for various diseases, keepers of geese can normally forget about these inconveniences. In mild climates geese require no special housing, and even in cold northern areas, a simple windbreak or shed is often all that is necessary. Geese also do well in hot climates as long as there is plenty of drinking water and shade.

EXCELLENT FORAGERS

Geese are the only domestic fowl that can live and reproduce on a diet of grass, water and grit. When succulent grass is available, geese need little more than drinking water if top growth and egg production are not desired.

In a research project conducted in the central mountains of tropical Puerto Rico where green grass is available the year around, a flock of Chinese geese were kept in a large pasture containing a quarter-acre pond. For twelve months these birds were given no supplemental feed in any form. While they produced only one-third as many eggs as a control group that was provided laying pellets, the grass-fed geese remained in good health and adequate flesh, and their eggs hatched fairly well.

UTILIZE WASTED LAND AND FOODS

Wet lowlands and marshes that normally go unused provide an abundant source of natural foods for waterfowl. Geese can also be turned out into harvested fields of corn, rice, wheat, barley and other crops where they will pick up shattered grain. Not only are the birds fattened, but the bothersome problem of volunteer plants in subsequent crops is reduced. Vegetable trimmings, garden and table leftovers, canning refuse and stale baked goods are relished by geese as well.

Active grazers, geese of all ages can be raised with a minimum of supplemental feed when succulent green grass is plentiful.

WEEDERS AND LAWN MOWERS

Geese eat many noxious weeds and grasses. When managed properly, they are an excellent organic means for eradicating unwanted plant growth in some crops. (See Appendix F, Using Geese as Weeders.) Geese can also be used as lawnmowers, particularly along hard-to-get ditches and fence rows and in orchards. When run in orchards, geese reduce diseases and harmful insects by cleaning up windfall fruits.

FAST GROWING

Of all birds commonly raised for meat, geese are considered the fastest growing. When well fed, large breed goslings from good stock are capable of weighing ten to twelve pounds in only eight to ten weeks after hatching. Goslings are also efficient converters of feed into meat. If managed properly, they can produce one pound of body weight for every 2.25 to 3.5 pounds of concentrated feed consumed.

TABLE 2   COMPARATIVE MEAT PRODUCTION OF POULTRY

Bird	Optimum Butchering Age weeks	Average Live Wt. at Butchering pounds	Feed Consump- tion pounds	Feed to Produce 1 Lb. of Bird pounds
Chicken, Broiler	8	4.0	8.5	2.1
Duck, Pekin	7	7.0	19.0	2.7
Goose, Embden	10-12	12.2	35.0	2.9
Turkey, Lg. White	16-20	17.0	55.0	3.2
Quail, Coturnix	6	.4	1.5	3.8
Guinea Fowl	12-18	2.3	11.0	4.8

Based on meat yields of quality stock which were fed concentrated feeds, kept in confinement and managed for efficient production. Growth rate and feed conversion are highly dependent on the quality of the birds and their care.

USEFUL EGGS

Geese usually are not thought of as proficient layers. However, some strains of the Chinese breed will average 60 to well over 100 eggs per goose per year. At five to six ounces per egg, that makes a lot of eating!

While goose eggs are widely acknowledged as being excellent for use in baked goods, there seems to be some bias against them for general eating purposes. From my observations, this prejudice appears to be mostly a problem of the head and not the palate. Over the last fifteen years, we've served goose eggs to meal guests and have received nothing but compliments. If we know someone "thinks" they don't like goose eggs, we don't mention that the scrambled, creped or souffled eggs they're eating at our table aren't of the chicken variety. We've never had any complaints! (For some of our favorite goose egg dishes, see Appendix D.)

TABLE 3   COMPARATIVE EGG PRODUCTION OF POULTRY

Bird	Egg Weight per Dozen ounces	Annual Egg Production #	Annual Egg Production pounds	Annual Feed Consump- tion pounds a	Annual Feed Consump- tion pounds b	Feed to Produce 1 Pound of Egg pounds	Efficient Production Life of Hens years
Duck, Campbell	31.0	288*	46.5	110	140	2.4-3.0	2-3
Quail, Coturnix	5.5	306	8.8	—	22	2.5	1
Chicken, Leghorn	24.0	240*	30.0	85	95	2.8-3.2	1-2
Goose, China	66.0	72	24.8	130	185	5.2-7.5	4-8
Guinea Fowl	17.0	78	6.9	45	65	6.5-8.7	1-2
Chicken, Broiler	25.0	144	18.8	125	130	6.6-6.9	1-2
Turkey, Lg. White	38.0	90	17.8	180	200	10.1-11.2	1-2

Based on the egg yields of good stock fed concentrated feeds and managed for efficient production. Egg size, egg production and feed conversion of poultry are highly dependent upon the quality of the birds and the care they receive.
*These rates of production are typical. However, under excellent management, some Leghorn flocks average 270-290 eggs per hen and some Campbell flocks, 310-340 eggs per duck.
a—For hens that are free to roam and forage.
b—For hens raised in confinement.

AQUATIC PLANT CONTROL

Geese are useful in controlling the growth of grass on banks of ponds and streams, and various underwater plants such as widgeon grass, pondweed, bulrush and eelgrass. Depending on the climate and density of vegetation, four to eight geese are recommended per acre of water surface. When green algae and duckweed are a problem, five to ten ducks per square acre of water should be employed along with the geese. In my experience, neither geese nor ducks are effective in checking the growth of tropical water-lettuce or water-hyacinth. In fact, evidence indicates that waterfowl can spread water-lettuce from infested to clean bodies of water.

VALUABLE FEATHERS AND DOWN

Goose feathers and down are considered by many to be the best filler available, either natural or synthetic, for comforters, sleeping bags and winter clothing. (See Appendix E, Using Feathers and Down.)

SENTINELS

Geese — especially the Chinese breed — are extremely alert and will honk loudly at the appearance of strangers — be they persons or animals. Geese were acclaimed as "watchdogs" as early as 309 B.C. when they were credited with saving Rome from an attempted sneak attack by the Gauls. Today, watch geese are employed throughout the world by homesteaders, farmers and various industries.

Geese can add dignified beauty to all settings.

Young geese are easily tamed and make personable companions.

LONGEVITY

With a lifespan of fifteen to twenty years being fairly common, geese can be expected to outlive other types of fowl. (While difficult to document, there are reports of geese living 100 years). When young breeding stock is acquired, they normally reproduce at least five to six years, and often considerably longer under small flock conditions.

PERSONABLE

When kept in small flocks, most geese are friendly and make good pets. If hand reared, they often become as companionable as a puppy and will follow their owner wherever possible. An acquaintance of our family raised a single goose from little up, and this bird would on occasion sneak away from home and could be seen trailing his young master through town or to school.

DECORATIVE AND ENTERTAINING

With their large size, dignified actions and devoted family life, few domestic birds are more decorative or entertaining than geese. A few of these stately waterfowl add a great deal of beauty and interest to ponds, creeks and homesteads, and their ringing honks add a pleasing wild touch to any setting.

CHAPTER 2

Some Points To Consider

There's no doubt about it — the goose is an exceptionally practical and sturdy critter that adapts to most environments. But to help avoid unpleasant surprises, there are several facts I think you should know if you've never raised geese.

SIZE AND TEMPERAMENT

Geese are large birds, and pound for pound, are stronger than most animals. While certainly not a threat to a person's life, a harassed or angry adult goose can express its sentiments well with powerful bill and pounding wings. Fortunately, unless they have been teased or mistreated, geese normally are not aggressive except when nesting or brooding young. Even during these times of stress, most — if not all — unpleasant encounters can be avoided if a few behavioral characteristics of geese are understood by their keeper (see Chapter 4).

During the breeding season, it should be explained to small children that the goose pen or nesting area is best observed from a safe distance. Nesting geese seem to be more aggressive towards little people than to adults. If a child should stumble upon a pair of nesting birds, the youngster can be severely frightened, as well as painfully bruised. When a large person spars with a provoked goose, the greatest injury is usually to one's pride.

NOISE

The honking of geese is a welcome sound to most folks. If, however, you have close neighbors or live in town or suburbia, the trumpeting of these feathered buglers might not be appreciated. Some breeds are considerably noisier than others — with the Chinese and African leading the way. A small gaggle consisting of one of the calmer breeds — such as American Buffs, Pilgrims or Toulouse — will be reasonably quiet.

OVERCROWDED PONDS

A heavy concentration of geese on ponds or along creeks encourages unsanitary conditions and can damage bodies of water. While searching for roots and bulbs, geese drill with their bills in soft soil or mud around the water's edge. High densities of geese will muddy water, hasten bank erosion and destroy plant life. However, a sensible number of birds (twenty to forty per acre of water surface) helps control aquatic plant growth and does not significantly accelerate bank deterioration.

GARDENS

Just about every fruit and vegetable that we humans relish, geese also find tasty. Except for certain crops that can be successfully weeded by geese, having a goose in the garden is almost as undesirable as a fox in the henhouse. If you wish to be both a successful goose herder and gardener, the birds or the vegetables and flowers will need to be fenced in with an adequate barrier. Fortunately, geese are not accomplished high jumpers and can usually be controlled with a twenty-four- to thirty-six-inch fence, especially if the flight feathers of one wing have been clipped.

PLUCKING

Any way you look at it, defeathering slaughtered geese is a bigger job than picking chickens. I am not a particularly fast feather puller, but for comparison, it takes me three to five minutes to hand pick a scalded chicken and fifteen to twenty minutes for a young goose. Some people claim that it takes half a day to deplume a large goose, but if it takes even a novice more than thirty minutes, there's a good chance that the bird was not in proper feather condition for plucking or an improvement could be made in technique.

TABLE 4   APPROXIMATE COMPOSITION OF VARIOUS MEATS

Description	Calories per 100 grams	Protein %	Fat %
Chicken: raw			
Fryers			
Total edible	155	17.3	7.4
Flesh only	107	19.3	2.7
Roasters			
Total edible	239	19.2	17.9
Flesh only	131	21.1	4.5
Mature hens and cocks			
Total edible	298	17.4	24.8
Flesh only	155	21.6	7.0
Turkey: raw			
Total edible	218	20.1	14.7
Flesh only	162	24.0	6.6
Duckling: domestic, raw			
Total edible	326	16.0	28.6
Flesh only	165	21.4	8.2
Duck: wild, raw			
Total edible	233	21.1	15.8
Flesh only	138	21.3	5.2
Goose: domestic, raw			
Total edible	354	16.4	31.5
Flesh only	159	22.3	7.1
Rabbit: raw			
Flesh only	162	21.0	8.0
Pork: raw			
Carcass (medium-fat class)			
Total edible	513	10.2	52.0
Composition of trimmed lean cuts, ham, loin, shoulder and spareribs (medium-fat class)			
Total edible	308	15.7	26.7
Beef: raw			
Carcass			
Total edible			
Choice grade	379	14.9	35.0
Good grade	323	16.5	28.0
Total edible, trimmed to retail levels			
Choice grade	301	17.4	25.1
Good grade	263	18.5	20.4

*Information from *Handbook of the Nutritional Contents of Foods.*

GOOSE MEAT AND EGGS

All types of poultry supply food that is nutritious and tasty. However, there are variations in flavor, texture and composition of the meat and eggs produced by the various species. People also have differing tastes and dietary

TABLE 5   APPROXIMATE COMPOSITION OF EGGS

Kind of Egg	Protein %	Fat %	Cholesterol* mg/gm of egg	Calories per 100 gms
Chicken, Commercial Egg	12.9	11.5	4.94-5.50	163
Chicken, Commercial Broiler	—	—	6.38	—
Quail, Coturnix	11.5	10.9	8.44	186
Turkey	13.1	11.8	9.33	170
Duck	13.3	14.5	8.84	191
Goose	13.9	13.3	—	185

Information from *Handbook of the Nutritional Contents of Foods* and "Cholesterol Content of Market Eggs," *Poultry Science Journal*.
*Young hens produce eggs with less cholesterol than old hens.
NOTE: Dashes indicate that information was not available.

needs. If you're planning to raise geese for home use, but have never eaten them, I suggest that you sample goose products before starting your own flock. (This is a good idea before spending time and money on any type of unfamiliar animal for food.) The following observations are presented to help you evaluate your first encounters with goose cuisine.

- For roasting, young geese that are six months or less are much preferred over older birds by most people.
- Chinese and African geese produce meat that is less fatty than other breeds. There are also differences in the color and texture of the skin and meat among the various breeds.
- If geese consume strong-flavored foods, their meat and eggs can be adversely affected. Examples of situations where this can occur are birds that feed in waterways full of aquatic animal life or weeder geese that have been used in a crop such as mint.
- The meat of goslings raised in close confinement and pushed for top growth is much greasier than that of birds which have foraged for some of their food and have grown at a slower pace.
- Goose eggs are fine for most uses, and are considered by many chefs to be the best eggs for baked goods. The albumen is firmer than in chicken eggs, and normally does not whip as well.

CHAPTER 3

External Features

From a physical standpoint, geese just might be the most versatile animals on earth. With their webbed toes, moderately long legs and strong wings, this member of the waterfowl family is equally at home swimming on water, strolling on land or flying through the open sky. Being familiar with the prominent external features of geese is not only a useful management tool but will also increase your respect for these remarkable fowl.

BODY SHAPE

In contrast to the deep, V-shaped bodies of land fowl such as chickens and guineas, the underbodies of geese are wider and flatter, providing stability and minimal drag while swimming and flying.

FEATHERS

When plucking a goose, one cannot help but marvel at the variety and density of feathers. While amateur goose pickers are often intimidated by the sheer quantity of feathers, it's this characteristic that allows geese to swim in icy waters and survive subzero temperatures.

Nomenclature of Geese

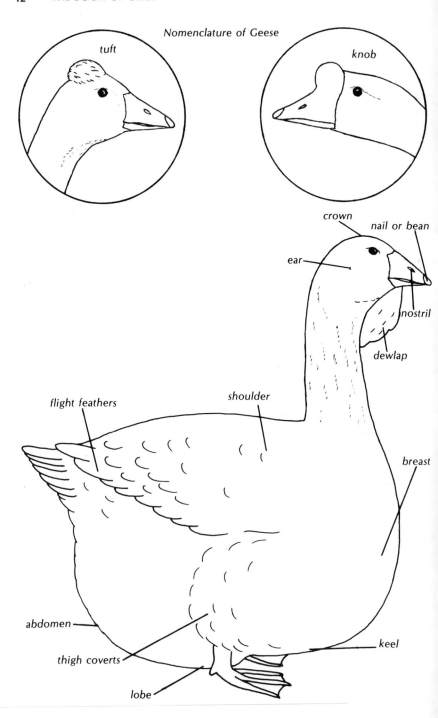

Despite the diverse assortment of sizes and shapes, all feathers fall into four main categories. Most numerous and visible are the contour feathers which cloak the body, ranging from the tiny tufts of the neck to the large plumes of the back and sides. Underneath these lies the insulating down which is highly valued as filler for cold weather clothing and bedding. Scattered across the skin surface are hairlike filoplumes which grow to several inches in length. While the function of these filaments is not fully understood, it is believed that they serve as sensory receptors. The stiff flight feathers of the wings and tail provide lift, thrust and steering while birds are airborne.

To keep their garb in good condition through a year of wear and tear, geese spend hours each day preening. Hidden under the feathers at the base of the tail is an oil gland that produces a feather conditioner and water repellent. As geese groom themselves, they comb the excretion onto the feathers with their bill.

WINGS

Geese have powerful pinions that are long and broad, with wingspans of sixty to seventy-six inches being typical. At the wrist on the leading edge of each wing, mature birds have a small, blunt knob which is used as a weapon when geese are fighting or defending themselves. To avoid being flogged with these dull spurs when catching and holding geese, the wings must be restrained firmly. (See Chapter 9 for proper methods of catching and holding.)

TAIL

For their impressive body size, geese have short rudders — approximately five to eight inches in length. Birds of either sex with tails that droop below the line of the back — except for Canadas and Egyptians — or ganders that have lost their tail feathers due to fighting, normally cannot be relied upon to produce good fertility.

BILL

Equipped with powerful bills, geese are well adapted for grazing, pulling up underwater plants, probing damp soil for buried roots and bulbs, and pinching the backside of anyone who stumbles onto their nests or young. Unlike the broad, flattened bills of ducks, the bills of geese are thick at the base, narrow in the middle and tapered towards the end, terminating in a large, hard nail. On both sides of the bill there is a slight gap between the upper and lower mandibles, which exposes toothlike lamellae. These serrations give geese tremendous grip for pulling slippery vegetation from bottoms of ponds, grazing on tough grasses and hanging onto intruders.

Since geese are primarily grazers, their nostrils are located near the center of the bill in contrast to those of ducks which are near the head. (People occasionally ask how to distinguish ducklings from goslings. Other than body size, the location of the nostrils and the shape of the bill are two of the most reliable means of identification for the novice.)

Geese are well equipped for grazing and feeding on slippery aquatic plants with their powerful, serrated bills.

KNOB

The varieties of geese who trace their ancestory to the wild Swan Goose of Asia exhibit a prominent forehead knob at the base of their bills. These fleshy head adornments serve as breed trademarks for African and Chinese geese and make sexing mature birds of these breeds easier than most other varieties. Among specimens of the same strain and age, the knobs of males usually are considerably larger than those of females. Knobs become noticeable at three to five months of age and continue to develop for several years.

If furnished a windbreak, knobbed geese can winter comfortably outside in subfreezing weather. However, since knobs are subject to frostbite, it is advantageous to provide these birds with a protective shelter they can enter at will when temperatures fall below 10° to 0° F (-14° C) for extended periods of time.

EYES

Geese have exceptional eyesight. Many times — often without success — I've strained to glimpse what object a flock of geese with craned necks were so intently watching high in the sky. Not only can they see great distances, but, due to the position of their eyes, they also have a wide field of vision. With just a slight turn of their head, they get a full 360°-view of the world about them.

DEWLAP

A loose fold of feather-covered skin hanging from the throat and upper neck is present on mature specimens of African and standard Toulouse geese, and occasionally on individuals of other breeds. Like knobs, the main functions of dewlaps are cosmetic and for breed identification. Dewlaps increase in size as geese age, often not appearing on goslings until they are three to six months old.

NECK

The elongated necks of geese help them keep a watchful eye on the surrounding countryside and bring into reach a wide variety of foods. They can feed on submerged aquatic plants, grab fruit from trees and bushes, snatch seed heads from tall grasses and reach through coarse fencing to nibble on garden crops!   •

FEET AND LEGS

With moderately long legs and webbed toes, geese are equally at-home swimming or walking. All four toes on each foot, including the small back toe, have a claw. While these nails are usually worn down and quite blunt, they can inflict nasty scratches across unprotected arms if birds are held without their

With their strong legs and webbed toes, geese are equally at home on land or water. These Tufted Romans are owned by Curtis Oakes, Cochranton, Pennsylvania.

legs being properly restrained. The legs of geese are stronger than those of ducks, but still are more easily injured than those of chickens. To avoid crippling, geese should be caught and held by their necks and/or bodies, not by the legs.

KEEL

It is not uncommon for a mature goose to develop a keel. These pendulous folds of skin are not a sign of disease or ill health, but are the result of tame geese having easy access to feed while not getting the rigorous exercise of their wild brethren. Well-developed keels are a breed characteristic of standard Toulouse, but are not preferred on other breeds.

LOBES

When well fed, geese of most European breeds develop two lobes that hang between their legs from the abdomen. Aesthetically, it is preferred that these folds be the same size; however, unbalanced lobes do not indicate lower productivity or illness. The number of lobes is usually not an accurate means for determining gender, but mature females often — although certainly not always — have larger lobes than males.

Smooth, lobeless abdomens are called for in the African and Chinese breeds. Still, Africans — particularly females — frequently have double lobes, and mature Chinese geese often reveal a single lobe especially during the laying season. A single lobe is considered an important breed characteristic of authentic Pomeranian geese, but dual lobes are often observed on specimens carrying this name.

CHAPTER 4

Behavior

In the poultry clan, the goose is at the top of the honor roll when it comes to intelligence. While personalities and habits do vary considerably among individual birds, most geese exhibit certain behavioral patterns which should be understood if you're going to raise them successfully.

PECKING ORDER

The pecking order is a universal bird law which allows individual geese to live peacefully within a gaggle. In its simplest form, the top bird in a flock can peck or dominate all others, the number two bird can dominate all but number one, the number three bird can dominate all but numbers one and two, and on down the line until the last individual — who dominates no one.

When a new goose is introduced into a gaggle, the pecking order is threatened, resulting in a power struggle which may provoke fighting. Unless birds are being seriously wounded in the fracas, don't interfere since this quarrel is needed for peaceful coexistence in the future.

RESPONSE TO FEAR

To grow well and to reproduce successfully, geese must remain calm. Geese have good memories and do not quickly forget people, animals or situations that scare them. After being badly frightened, they may not settle down completely for several days or even weeks. Because they are sensitive to the sight and sound of death, whenever geese need to be killed — either for butchering or due to illness or injury — it is advisable to dispatch birds out of sight and hearing of the flock.

FEEDING

Geese are grazers. Their natural diet consists almost entirely of grasses, seeds, roots, bulbs, berries and fruits, supplemented with a minimum of animal matter such as insects and snails. When good quality forage is available, geese can survive and reproduce without supplemental feeding of grains and concentrated feeds. Sand and small gravel are picked up to aid the gizzard in grinding hard seeds and fibrous grasses. When feeding on water, geese use their long necks to reach submerged aquatic plants.

SWIMMING

Strong and graceful swimmers, geese are able to take to water as soon as they leave the nest. However, to avoid drowning losses, goslings must never be allowed to bathe where they cannot exit easily. In fact, in most situations it is best to keep the downy young out of all water until they are three to four weeks old. While geese usually maintain a neater appearance when swimming water is available, they certainly can be raised successfully without it.

Geese of many breeds are devoted parents, with both the goose and the gander helping to rear the young.

WALKING

Strong walkers, geese can cover long distances on foot in a surprisingly short time. To keep them from wandering off, mature geese usually need to be confined, particularly the first few weeks after being moved to a new home.

FLYING

Despite their large size, many domestic breeds have retained at least a portion of their flying skills. While standard Toulouse and Sebastopols normally have difficulty rising clear of the ground, most other varieties can become airborne, especially if they are not overweight and have a downhill runway or a headwind to assist their liftoff.

In a vocational poultry program in Puerto Rico, we kept breeding flocks of production Toulouse, Embdens and Chinese geese in a spacious, hilly pasture. At feeding time, the birds would sometimes be grazing out of sight behind a knoll. But when called, they would often come flying from distances of several hundred yards. It was always a thrill to watch these majestic birds wing their way over the rolling terrain and ski to a stop on the pond below the feeding station.

MATING

The bond between male and female is stronger in geese than in other domestic fowl. Changing mates can be difficult, often requiring several weeks or months, especially if the old consorts cannot be kept out of each other's sight or earshot. When one member of a pair dies or is disposed of, the remaining bird sometimes refuses a new mate, and on occasion has even been known to die. However, most geese (even Canadas which are noted for fidelity) will eventually accept a new mate after a period of mourning.

The number of geese a gander can be expected to service varies from one in Canadas and Egyptians to four to six in Chinese. (See recommended mating ratios for each breed in Chapter 5.) It is important that there are not too many males in a flock during the breeding season. If there are, the result can be low fertility due to fighting or from the ganders banding together in bachelor groups. Also, the backs and heads of females can be denuded and lacerated from excessive mating activities. As ganders get older, they sometimes will copulate only with one or two favorite mates. A goose that is receiving her mate's attention can usually be identified by a bare patch on the back of her head where feathers have been pulled out when the gander mounts for mating.

If raised separately as goslings, mature geese of different breeds will often remain segregated even when kept in a common pasture. However, if you keep several varieties and wish to raise purebred offspring, it is wise to pen each breed separately at least four weeks prior to and throughout the breeding season. Chinese and commercial type Africans are especially prone to cross-breeding.

While most geese can copulate successfully on land, they prefer mating on water. The majority of our breeders have been kept without swimming water being available, and over the years, the fertility rate of their eggs has averaged 85 to 90 percent. Nevertheless, the larger breeds, especially deep-keeled standard Toulouse, normally have higher fertility if they have access to bathing water at least fifteen inches deep.

NESTING

Geese are ground nesters, often selecting a nesting sight that is in the open or next to a tree or fence post. Natural nests are shallow depressions in the turf, lavishly lined with grass, straw and leaves. When sufficient nesting materials are not within easy reach, geese will sometimes carry it to the nest in their bills. If eggs are left for natural incubation, females pluck down from their breasts for added insulation and to better expose their warm bodies to the eggs. While the goose is in charge of the incubation chores, her mate usually stands guard until the eggs hatch and then assists in rearing the goslings.

The natural clutch size for geese ranges from five to fifteen eggs.

DEFENDING NESTS AND YOUNG

Because they are devoted parents, most geese become aggravated if intruders approach too closely to their nest or young. During this sensitive period, the goosekeeper should recognize the birds' strong territorial instincts, and take several precautions to help avoid unpleasant confrontations.

The first step that can be taken is to encourage geese to nest where they can be left in peace. This means placing nests or nesting material as far away as possible from gates, doorways and well-traveled paths. The second step is to molest nesting geese no more than absolutely necessary. Thirdly, if the nest or goslings must be approached, always move slowly, talking quietly and reassuringly to the birds.

Normally, geese are more bark than bite. If they come charging at you hissing with their necks snaking along the ground or their wings spread open, usually the best response is to stop and stand still. After the birds have settled down, continue your advance. By using this stop and start strategy, most nesting geese can be approached without a single lick being inflicted.

While some people like to dive in and get the job done quickly, in my experience, fast movements startle the birds and rouse them to defend their nest or young with reckless abandon. And remember, geese tend to get nastier after each skirmish.

One last word — when walking away from brooding geese, do so slowly and without turning your back to the birds. There's nothing like a turned back to bring out all the bravado in an anxious bird.

Because they take their parental duties seriously, geese normally become aggravated if intruders approach too closely to their nest or young.

FIGHTING

Unless overcrowded conditions exist or there are an excessive number of males, geese normally live harmoniously among themselves and with other creatures. When a new bird is introduced into an established flock, a period of chasing and face to face combat may take place, especially if the newcomer is a gander. Ordinarily, ganders will not quarrel among themselves if geese are not present.

LIFE EXPECTANCY

Geese have the longest lifespan of commonly raised fowl. The exact number of years they will reproduce or live is impossible to specify since there is a wide variation among breeds and individual birds within the same breed. When protected from predators and accidental deaths, it is not uncommon for geese to live fifteen to twenty years, with extraordinary birds living considerably longer. Normally, domestic geese reach peak egg production during their third, fourth and fifth years, and ganders are the most fertile between the ages of two to five. When well cared for, geese that are raised in small flocks can be expected to reproduce satisfactorily longer than under commercial conditions. In general, Canada geese live and reproduce longer than fully domesticated breeds, sometimes producing young for thirty years or more.

CHAPTER 5

Selecting A Breed

Novices often presume all geese are pretty much alike, except that some are white and others gray. In actuality, geese are a diverse lot and come in an assortment of colors, sizes, shapes and temperaments and have varied producing abilities. Spending a few minutes at the outset in acquainting yourself with the characteristics of each breed will help eliminate the unpleasant surprises that sometimes confront uninformed beginners.

IMPORTANT CONSIDERATIONS

To identify the features needed in geese for your flock, I feel there are five main questions that you should consider.

- *What is your main purpose for raising geese?* Is it for eggs, meat, feathers, weed eradication, aquatic plant control, sentinel, decoration or a combination of these and other aims?
- *Where are you located?* Some breeds, particularly Chinese and African, are more talkative than others — a fact which should be taken into account when you have close neighbors. Also, some geese are not as well adapted to extremely cold or wet weather.
- *How much experience do you have raising waterfowl?* Several breeds, including Dewlap Toulouse, Sebastopol, Canada and Egyptian, demand special care and know-how to be raised successfully. In my opinion, these varieties should be avoided by most beginners until several years' experience has been acquired with other geese.

- *What plumage color is best adapted to your situation?* Aside from personal preferences, color is significant for several practical reasons. The pin feathers of light-plumaged birds are not as visible as those with dark plumage, making it easier to obtain an attractive carcass with light-colored geese when they are butchered. On the other hand, dark birds are better camouflaged, making them less susceptible to predators. Also, if there is no bathing water available, colored geese maintain a neater appearance than white ones.
- *Which breeds are available either locally or by mail-order?* Some types are less common, making them more expensive and difficult to obtain.

THE BREEDS

While all tame varieties of true ducks trace their lineage to a single source in the Mallard, domestic geese were developed from two distinct species: the Asian Swan Goose and the European Graylag. Most of the purebred geese being raised in North America belong to one of nine breeds. The descendents of the Swan Goose include the African and Chinese, while Embden, Pilgrim, Toulouse, American Buff, Pomeranian, Sebastopol and Tufted Roman are Graylag derivatives. In addition, two feral species — Canada and Egyptian — have been standardized by the American Poultry Association and are popular with hobbyists.

Swan geese, such as this gander and two geese, are believed to be the forerunners of the African and Chinese breeds. Owned by Bud Butcher, Canby, Oregon.

TABLE 6 BREED PROFILES

Category	Breed	Origin	Weight in Pounds M	Weight in Pounds F	Breeding Age in Years	Yearly Egg Production	Mothering Ability	Availability
Lightweight	Chinese	Asia	12	10	1	40-100+	Poor-Fair	Excellent
	Tufted Roman	Europe	12	10	1-2	25-35	Good	Fair
Mediumweight	American Buff	USA	18	16	1-2	25-35	Good	Good
	Pilgrim	USA	14	13	1-2	25-40	Good	Good
	Pomeranian	Germany	17	15	1-2	25-35	Good	Fair
	Sebastopol	Europe	14	12	1-2	25-35	Poor-Fair	Fair
Heavyweight	African	Asia	20	18	1-2	20-45	Fair-Good	Good
	Embden	Europe	26	20	1-2	25-35	Fair-Good	Excellent
	Toulouse Dewlap	France	26	20	2-3	20-35*	Poor-Fair	Fair
	Production	France	20	18	1-2	25-40	Fair-Good	Excellent
Ornamental	Canada	Canada	12	10	3-4	4-8**	Excellent	Good
	Egyptian	Africa	5½	4½	2-3	5-8**	Excellent	Fair

Information presented in this profile is based on the average characteristics of each breed. Actual performance of individual birds may vary considerably.

*Some breeders of Dewlap Toulouse have reported yields of 45 to over 60 eggs annually.

**Canada and Egyptian geese often will lay a second or even a third clutch if eggs are removed and incubated under a foster mother or in an incubator.

HEAVYWEIGHT BREEDS

African

Description — The bold, massive African is one of our most imposing breeds. Their heavy bodies, thick necks, stout bills and jaunty posture all combine to give the impression of strength and vitality.

Attached to the forehead of mature birds is a well-developed, forward inclining knob that requires several years to fully develop. Hanging from the lower jaw and upper neck is a smooth, crescent-shaped dewlap that often becomes rather jagged with age. The eyes are large and deep-set. The body, which is long, wide and deep, should be nearly the same thickness from front to back. Ideally, the underline is smooth, and free of keel or excessively baggy paunch. Smooth, rounded abdomens similar to those found in the Chinese breed are preferred, with restricted or no lobe development. Tails point up and are well-folded.

Two varieties of Africans are found in North America, the more common Gray (also known as Brown) and the rare White. In the colored variety, the plumage is a pleasing combination of browns, buffs, grays and white. The most conspicuous marking is a dark brown stripe that runs over the crown of the head and down the back of the neck. On mature birds, a narrow band of whitish feathers separates the satin-black bill and knob from the brown head. The legs and feet are dark orange to brownish orange.

At maturity, standard-bred Africans have large, trim bodies, well-developed dewlaps and forward inclining knobs. Owned by Bud Butcher, Canby, Oregon.

White Africans are much less common than the Grays, but are being improved by a number of waterfowl breeders, such as Stanley Osika, Crown Point, Indiana, owner of this pair.

White Africans have orange bills and knobs, bright orange shanks and feet, and white plumage. Because of their relative scarcity, Whites frequently are less refined in type and somewhat smaller than the Grays, although improvements are being made.

Selecting Breeders — When raising goslings, it's a good idea to mark those that grow the most rapidly so they can be saved for future breeding stock. Always look for massive features, good body size and carriage 30° to 40° above horizontal. The head should be large and broad between the eyes, with the knob being as wide as the head. Avoid birds with narrow heads, slender necks, shallow bodies, drooping tails, pronounced keels and baggy paunches that drag or nearly touch the ground when the bird is standing. Older females, especially during the laying season, will often have low-hung paunches and show some indication of a keel. However, to maintain the lean meat qualities of the African, males of all ages and young females kept for reproduction should be keelless and have only moderately full abdomens. Tails held in line with the back, or lower, are often an indication of physical weakness and low fertility in this breed.

Comments — Combined with their burly beauty, Africans are the leanest of the heavyweight breeds and a favorite of many veteran goose breeders. Big, authentic specimens are relatively high-priced, but once seed stock is acquired, they are long-lived and will reproduce for many years under normal circumstances. Commercial Africans sold by most hatcheries are moderately priced, but often are underweight and little more than slightly oversized Chinese. Although some literature claims that Africans are a warm weather goose, they are hardy and can withstand considerable cold weather — confirmed by the fact that many of the leading breeders of this goose live in cold, northern climates. However, to protect their knobs from frostbite, a shelter such as a three-sided shed can be provided when temperatures fall into the teens. Frostbitten knobs of colored geese often develop orange patches that normally go away by the following autumn. Depending on the particular strain and individual birds, each gander can be mated with two to six geese.

Embden

Description — In North America, more Embdens are raised commercially than all other breeds combined. Their large size, rapid growth, white plumage and rugged constitution all contribute to their popularity.

Along with Dewlap Toulouse, authentic Embdens are considered the heaviest of all geese. They have large, oval heads; long, slightly arched necks; broad backs and long, deep bodies. The breast is smooth and keelless, the paunch double-lobed and the tail carried slightly above the line of the back.

Adult birds should have pure white plumage, orange bills, shanks and feet, and blue eyes. Goslings in the downy stage are yellow with varying amounts of gray on their backs and heads. In my experience, purebred Embden goslings can always be sexed by the color of their down from the day they hatch until dilution genes whiten the plumage as they feather out. The gray markings on downy males are a discernibly lighter hue than that of the females. Young Embdens, like most white varieties of European geese, often have colored feathers in their juvenile plumage that normally are replaced with white plumes at maturity.

Selecting Breeders — Vigor, fast growth, and large bodies exhibiting good length, width and depth are most important. Avoid birds with weak heads, dewlaps, short necks, slipped wings, ponderous gaits, small size and young females and males of any ages with keels. While dual, balanced lobes are aesthetically preferred, birds with single or unbalanced lobes are not inferior from a practical standpoint.

Comments — Big, authentic Embdens are beautiful and an excellent choice when large roasting birds are desired. They dress cleanly when butchered, and some people prefer their white feathers and down for use in bedding and clothing. Because of their large size and active dispositions, it usually is not advisable to keep them in close confinement with other breeds of poultry. Ganders can normally be bred with three or four females.

Because of their fast growth, large size and white plumage, Embdens are the most common breed raised by commercial producers. Owned by Willow Hill Hatchery, Richland, Pennsylvania.

Production Toulouse

Description — Most of the gray geese seen on farms or around homesteads are Toulouse or crosses of this trusty old breed. While they are an adequate, all-around variety, it seems their popularity is due in part to wide availability and the fact that they are the one breed with which almost everyone is acquainted. For many people, goose and Toulouse are synonymous.

Good specimens have large, oval heads, moderately long, heavy necks and thick, wide bodies capable of carrying eighteen to twenty-six pounds of weight. (However, commercial Toulouse sold by many hatcheries often do not reach these weights.) Occasionally, mature birds develop small dewlaps under the throat. Like all breeds descended from the Graylag, the feathers on the sides of the neck are deeply furrowed.

This pair of gray geese and their five-week-old offspring are typical of the so-called production Toulouse sold by many hatcheries.

The over-all color scheme of the plumage is shades of gray, except for the abdomen which is off-white. The dark sides and back are traversed with lighter markings that give an attractive laced effect. An orange bill and reddish orange legs help brighten up an otherwise somber-colored bird.

Selecting Breeders — The Toulouse is a large utility breed, so fast growth and big, meaty bodies are of primary importance. Avoid birds with refined features, shallow or narrow bodies and weak heads. Being an all gray goose — except for the abdomen — white feathers anywhere else in the plumage are not preferred. However, foreign color does not decrease practical qualities.

Comments — Toulouse have long been noted as the best layers among the heavyweight breeds and for their ability to fatten readily when well fed in close confinement. In years past, when goose grease was extensively used in place of modern products such as margarine, vegetable oils and shortening, the ability to put on large quantities of fat was considered important.

While their dark plumage is a disadvantage if butchered when pin feathers are present, they are better camouflaged and do not appear unkempt as quickly as white geese. Ganders can normally service three to four geese.

A trio of Dewlap Toulouse which is in breeding condition. When fattened, the keels of some specimens nearly brush the ground. Owned by Bud Butcher, Canby, Oregon.

Standard Dewlap Toulouse

Description — The standard Dewlap Toulouse is a huge, blocky goose of unmatched proportions. When fat, some specimens tip the scales at thirty pounds or more. However, because of their loose plumage and deep keels, they often appear to be heavier than they are in actuality. Quiet and slow-moving, they normally do not wander far from where they are fed and watered.

Every feature of this placid giant is massive. The bill is stout, the head large and broad, while the moderately long neck is thick and nearly straight. Suspended from the lower bill and upper neck is a heavy, folded dewlap that increases in size and fullness for a number of years. The body is long, broad and deep, ending in a well-spread tail that points up slightly. When in good flesh, the rounded breast flows smoothly into a wide keel that in extreme cases nearly reaches the turf. The wide, ample paunch is double-lobed and often brushes the ground, particularly in females that are laying. When Dewlap Toulouse are relaxed, their carriage is nearly horizontal.

The original gray variety of standard Toulouse has the identical color scheme as production Toulouse. A new buff variety, which has been developed by Paul Lofland of Central Point, Oregon, is similar in color to the American Buff.

Selecting Breeders — If not carefully bred, all heavyweight breeds of geese can decrease in size each succeeding generation. The breeding of standard Toulouse is complicated further because their enormous bulk is combined with the unnatural characteristics of exaggerated keel and dewlap.

In the order of their importance, the major considerations when choosing breeders are vigor, adequate body size, high fertility, good egg production, depth of keel, smoothness of underline and proportions of the dewlap. Keep away from using birds that have narrow or undersized bodies, excessively arched backs, keels that have extremely rough underlines, slender necks, small dewlaps and weak heads. Except in mature geese that are laying, tails that are not held above the line of the back are often a sign of low fertility and a lack of vigor.

Comments — Dewlap Toulouse are probably the most challenging domestic goose to raise successfully. Seed stock is expensive, and for good reasons. Most Dewlap Toulouse do not reproduce consistently until two or three years of age. Even when in peak production, fertility and hatchability of eggs are often considerably lower than for other breeds, although productivity varies widely depending on management, strain and individual birds. With excellent management, some breeders are able to produce twenty or more goslings from some Dewlap Toulouse geese, but such records are the exception rather than the rule.

During the breeding season it is extremely important that producing birds are not overweight, but they do need an adequate supply of concentrated feed that is 18 to 22 percent crude protein. Fertility and hatchability are highest when birds get sufficient exercise and have access to succulent green feeds and swimming water a minimum of fifteen inches deep.

These big geese thrive on tranquility. To do well, they must be disturbed as seldom as possible and should not be penned in close confinement with active breeds of geese, ducks and other fowl. Matings consisting of pairs or trios are usually the most productive.

MEDIUMWEIGHT BREEDS

American Buff

Description — The unique color of the American Buff makes them one of the most colorful geese. On bright, sunny days, a flock of grazing Buffs is a pleasing scene. Furthermore, their serene nature makes them an enjoyable bird to have around.

In body conformation, Buffs are what you'd call the basic goose. They have medium-long necks, chunky bodies, dual lobes and little or no evidence of keels. The tail is held in line with or only slightly above the line of the back.

The color of their plumage is varying shades of buff, except for the abdomen which is nearly white. The feathers of the back and sides are edged with creamy white. Bills and feet are orange and the eyes brown.

Selecting Breeders — First consideration should be given to good body size. In color, a medium shade of buff that is free of gray tones is preferred.

The attractive American Buff is a good all around breed that adds color to the home flock. This fine pair bred by Curtis Oakes, owned by Willow Hill Hatchery, Richland, Pa.

While a back with even color is desirable, it should be noted that this portion of the plumage usually is somewhat checkered or mottled, even on most of today's best specimens. Avoid breeding from Buffs with pinched heads, small or shallow bodies, prominent keels, gray in the plumage and excessively faded or dark color. To produce the highest percentage of offspring with correct color, some breeders have found it helpful to use ganders that are slightly lighter in color than their standard-colored mates.

Comments — American Buffs are no-nonsense geese that are well suited for the average home flock. They are colorful, hardy, calm, good natural parents and make fine medium-large roasting birds. When butchered, they dress almost as cleanly as white geese. Their color also has the advantage of not soiling as readily as white plumage. Ganders can be mated with three to five geese.

Pilgrim

Description — The calm, personable Pilgrim is the only goose breed in which the gender of both goslings and mature birds can be distinguished by their color. Day-old males are silvery-yellow with light-colored bills, in contrast to the olive-gray females with their darker bills. Adult ganders are mostly white,

The mild natured Pilgrim is the only goose breed that can be sexed at any age by plumage color. Ganders are predominantly white, while geese are gray with white faces. Owned by Mother Hen Hatchery, Corvallis, Oregon.

usually with gray rumps (which are covered by the wings) and traces of color in the tail and wings. Mature geese are soft dove-gray with varying amounts of white in their faces. Bills and legs are orange in both sexes, while the eyes are blue in ganders and dark brown in geese.

Although somewhat smaller in size, Pilgrims are similar in type to the American Buff. The head is trim, often with a slightly flattened crown while the neck is average in length and thickness. Bodies are full and plump, with smooth keelless breast and dual lobes preferred.

Selecting Breeders — Some prominent poultry judges and waterfowl breeders warn against oversize in Pilgrims. However, from my observations, many strains are somewhat under standard weight, so I consider good-sized birds especially valuable for breeding. Look for broad backs and breasts that are keelless. Stay away from using birds with any sign of a knob (an indication of crossbreeding), long necks and legs, shallow breasts, ganders with excessive gray in the plumage and geese with predominantly white necks. All-white ganders from pure Pilgrim stock can be useful in keeping excessive color from cropping up in male offspring. Unlike other white geese derived from the Graylag, Pilgrim ganders often exhibit more color in their plumage after molting their juvenile garb. Because Pilgrims are noted for being sweet-tempered, this trait should be considered when retaining birds for reproduction.

Comments — Pilgrims are rugged, quiet, docile, good foragers, excellent natural parents and make good medium-sized roasting birds. Because they are sex-linked for color, it is a simple matter — even for the novice — to keep the correct ratio of males to females when selecting young for future breeders. Ganders can be mated with three to five geese. In situations where a medium-weight goose will suffice, I feel Pilgrims are the most practical choice for the home goose flock.

Pomeranian

Description — Once uncommon and seldom seen in most parts of North America, the multicolored Saddleback Pomeranian has been steadily gaining popularity over the last few years. They combine showy coloration with hardiness and medium-large bodies, making them a striking as well as practical breed.

If one can look past the colorful markings, a sturdily built goose is discovered. The chunky body exhibits a broad back and a deep breast. Unlike other breeds derived from the Graylag, Pomeranians are supposed to have but

Gray Saddleback Pomeranians, such as this handsome pair, are easily identified by their bold markings and reddish pink bills, legs and feet. Owned by Andrea Peterson, Oregon City, Oregon.

a single lobe hanging from the center of the paunch. However, due to genetic variations and crossbreeding in the past, geese carrying the Pomeranian name frequently exhibit two lobes.

In their homeland of Germany, Pomeranians have been raised in a number of varieties, including White, Gray and Saddleback. In North America, Saddlebacks are the only ones bred with frequency. The plumage of Gray Saddlebacks is predominantly white, with the head, upper neck, shoulders, back and flanks being brownish gray. Each colored feather of the back and flank is edged with near-white. Buff Saddlebacks are also bred and advertised. All Pomeranians should have pinkish red bills, reddish orange legs and blue eyes.

Except for plumage color, the rare Buff Saddleback Pomeranian should be identical to the Gray Saddleback. This pair owned by Bernard Lind, Umatilla, Oregon.

Selecting Breeders — Look for birds with chunky bodies and well-defined markings. When viewed from behind and above, the colored area of the back and shoulders should be reminiscent of the classic heart shape. Solid-colored heads are preferred, but most specimens have white feathers around the base of the bill. Some strains of Pomeranians produce birds with a slight indication of a knob at the base of the bill. This fault should be guarded against since it is evidence of crossbreeding. Also, avoid breeding from specimens with dewlaps, orange bills and feet, excessively white heads, dark feathers in the wings, and undersized bodies.

Comments — Pomeranians add color to goose flocks and are a good all-around breed for the home flock. While the plumage markings are fairly well fixed genetically, producing properly marked specimens is a challenge. Ganders can be mated with three to four geese.

Sebastopol

Description — Definitely a goose of a different feather, the crowning glory of Sebastopols is their long, soft curls. The plumage of no other waterfowl has been so drastically altered through selective breeding. In my opinion, a well-bred Sebastopol in good feather condition is one of the most amazing sights afforded by any domestic fowl. Combined with their unique appearance, they have a quiet nature, and when raised in small flocks and worked with gently, they become tame and make pleasant companions.

In body type, Sebastopols are a typical, medium-sized goose of the Graylag family. They have large, rounded heads, prominent eyes, slightly arched necks, keelless breasts and dual lobes. The plumage of the head and upper two-thirds of the neck is normal, while that of the breast and underbody is elongated and well-curled. The soft, fluffy feathers of the back, wings and tail have flexible shafts, are attractively spiraled, and in good specimens are so long that they nearly touch the ground.

To keep their unique plumage clean and attractive, Sebastopols need bathing water and should not be kept in close confinement with more aggressive birds. This pair owned by Curtis Oakes, Cochranton, Pennsylvania.

The standard variety is the White, which has snow-white plumage throughout (except in juveniles that often have traces of gray), orange bills and feet and brilliant blue eyes. Grays and Buffs are occasionally seen, but have a long way to go before they will approach the spectacular feathering displayed by White Sebastopols.

Selecting Breeders — Whenever a domestic animal is selected for an unnatural characteristic, great care must be taken to insure that vigor and fertility are not overlooked. Robust health and adequate size should be the first attributes sought for in Sebastopols. Next, look for birds with well-curled breast feathers, flexible flight feathers, and back and tail plumes that are long, broad and spiraled. Stay away from birds with crooked toes, slipped wings, straight, stiff flights, short or narrow back plumage and smooth, uncurled breast feathers.

Comments — While Sebastopols are more practical than they would appear to be at first glance, most are kept for decoration and pets. Because of their loose, open plumage, they will become dirty and unkempt if clean swimming water is not available for frequent bathing. While Sebastopols are hardy and are being raised successfully in cold climates, it is a good idea to provide more protection during wet, cold and windy weather than normally afforded other breeds. Ganders can be mated with one to four geese. If low fertility is experienced, clipping the long plumes of the back and tail and the feathers around the vent is sometimes helpful.

LIGHTWEIGHT BREEDS

Chinese

Description — Often referred to as "Swan Geese" because of their dignified movements on land and water, Chinese are considered by many to be the most graceful and beautiful member of the goose family. In popularity they rival Toulouse and Embdens.

Combined with their ornamental qualities, Chinese are exceptionally practical. Of all breeds, they are the best layers, most active foragers (making them economical and useful as weeders), produce the least greasy meat, and, except for Pilgrims, are the easiest to sex at maturity. Because of their alert and talkative nature, they are frequently used as "watchdogs."

In type, Chinese are a picture of refinement and curves. Their bills are fairly long and slender, with a large, rounded, erect knob attached to the forehead. The trim head is held high and flows smoothly into a long, slim neck that is distinctively arched. Carried noticeably upright, the body is short and compact, with a prominent and well-rounded chest. The smooth breast is free of keel, and the moderately full abdomen is lobeless, except during the laying season when geese frequently disclose a single, centrally hung lobe. The position of the tail — which should be held high, especially in mature ganders — is a good indication of vitality. Due to their close-fitting plumage, Chinese are often heavier than they appear.

White Chinese are noted for stylish conformation, alertness and high egg yields. Owned by Willow Hill Hatchery, Richland, Pennsylvania.

Chinese are bred in two handsome varieties — the original, but less common Brown and the commercially preferred White. The latter variety has pure white plumage that's nicely offset by bright orange feet, knobs and bills, and clear blue eyes. While goslings of white European breeds are predominantly gray with yellow trim, the down of day-old White Chinese is vivid canary yellow.

The elegant Brown Chinese, which is often the choice of small flock owners, has rich brown and fawn plumage that is accentuated by a dark, russet-brown neck stripe. In mature birds, the glossy black bill and knob are separated from the main head plumage by a narrow band of creamy-white feathers. The shanks and feet are brownish orange or dark orange and the eyes brown.

Selecting Breeders — Look for compact bodies with prominent chests and keelless breasts, wings that fold in front of an erect tail, slender and symetrically arched necks and large, round knobs that rise well above the crown of the head. A spry, upright carriage is important in Chinese since it is a sign of good health and vigor. Avoid breeding from specimens with drooping shoulders, roach backs, deformed necks and long bodies. Common color faults that should be guarded against in the Browns are white flight feathers, white breast patches, yellow in the knob or bill (unless caused by frostbite), back and side feathers that are not distinctly edged or laced and faded neck and head stripes.

With their refined features and delicate coloration, Brown Chinese are considered by many people to be the most beautiful member of the domestic goose family. Outstanding old goose bred by the late Henry K. Miller.

Comments — Both from the standpoint of initial outlay and upkeep, this is the most economical breed of geese. With good management, the average Chinese goose produces nearly twice as many goslings as other geese, making day-old and mature stock the least expensive to buy. Because of their size and foraging ability, they require the least amount of supplemental feeding. However, while many people are attracted to Chinese, others find their talkativeness, active dispositions or lean meat undesirable. While they are hardy, due to their knobs which will freeze when temperatures fall below 20° to 25° F (-5° C), some breeders give them more protection during freezing weather than knobless breeds. Ganders can service four to six geese.

Roman Tufted

Description — The two classic features of the charming Roman Tufted are its small body size and unusual head adornment. This is a quiet and gentle little goose, the smallest of all domestic derivatives of the Graylag. And unlike any other breed, resting snugly on top of the head and just behind the eyes is a rounded or oblong tuft of feathers.

Roman Tufted have compact bodies, moderately long necks that are only slightly arched, keelless breasts and restricted lobe development. White is the preferred color, but goslings are sometimes produced with varying amounts of gray or buff in their adult plumage. First-year birds frequently exhibit some color which normally is molted out at maturity. Bills and legs are reddish-orange or pinkish, the eyes blue.

Selecting Breeders — Look for robust birds with calm, pleasant dispositions, small, compact bodies, and large tufts that are centrally placed on the head and that rise well above the skull. The front edge of the tuft should be over the back of the eyes. Avoid specimens with oversized bodies, keels, pronounced paunches and small, misshapened or misplaced tufts.

A pretty pair of Tufted Romans displaying head adornments of typical size and shape. Owned by Andrea Peterson, Oregon City, Oregon.

Since all Roman Tufted bred in North America apparently are descendents of a small group of birds, the genetic pool of this breed is limited. Every effort should be made to eliminate from the breeding flock birds with genetic defects such as crooked toes, wry tails, kinked necks and lack of vigor. If geese with such blemishes are bred from, these abnormalities will be intensified in following generations and the entire breed will suffer.

Comments — A flock of these petite, snow-white geese grazing in a lush, green pasture is a memorable sight. Despite their small stature, they produce a plump roasting bird. Although the size and shape of tufts varies, most goslings produced from pure stock have the headpiece. Ganders can be mated with two to four geese.

ORNAMENTAL

Canada

Description — Few native North American birds are as majestic as the Canada goose. The sight and sound of honking flocks winging their way across the sky is a delight enjoyed by people from coast to coast.

Canada geese are kept primarily for their stately beauty. This pair of Common Canadas owned by Bud Butcher, Canby, Oregon.

Canadas occasionally mate with geese of other species, resulting in sterile offspring, such as this Canada x Toulouse hybrid.

Canadas are a study in alertness, strength and agility. Long, sinuous necks give them a good view of the surrounding countryside and permit them to feed on deep-growing aquatic plants. Their muscular bodies are long, wide and flattened. Relatively long legs that are centrally positioned on the body give good maneuverability on land.

Many subspecies of Canadas exist, ranging in size from the tiny three- to five-pound Cackling's and Richardson's to the Giant or Maxima Honkers that occasionally tip the scales at eighteen pounds or more. Most of the semidomestic Canadas kept in captivity are of the Common (sometimes called Eastern) subspecies, and they typically weigh eight to twelve pounds. All Canadas have black bills, necks, tails and feet, and white abdomens and cheek markings. The color of the underbody varies from light brownish gray on the Common to very dark gray on most western subspecies.

Selecting Breeders — Canadas normally do not reproduce until three or four years of age. However, they frequently choose mates the first or second year after hatching. For consistent breeding success, unrelated birds need to be provided for pairings. Some breeders insist that the gander must be older than the goose, while others have not found this to be true.

When individuals of the same subspecies are mated, they normally produce offspring that are true in type and color. It is a good idea to avoid specimens that are over or undersized or who exhibit atypical coloration or body conformation.

Comments — Most Canada geese raised in captivity are kept for decoration and entertainment. Their dignified appearance, interesting habits and ringing voices add a touch of wild beauty to any setting. When succulent grasses are available, they require minimal quantities of supplemental feed. Some people have found them to be an economical source of meat.

To legally have Canadas in one's possession a permit is required, which is supplied — usually free of charge — by the person from whom the birds are acquired. The permit gives you the right to own and breed this game bird. However, if you ever wish to sell or even give away Canadas, you must first obtain a game bird dealer's license. Ignoring this regulation can result in stiff penalties. For more details, contact your nearest Fish and Wildlife Service Office.

Canadas normally mate in pairs, although semidomestic ganders have been known to take two geese. Contrary to popular belief, when one bird of a pair of Canadas is lost, the survivor will often take a new mate after a period of mourning. Unless they are free to range over a fairly large area (½ acre or more) throughout the breeding season, individual breeding pairs usually must be separated from all other birds with strong fencing at least four feet high. Canadas are extremely territorial while nesting and brooding young, and if stray goslings from another pair or smaller adult birds such as ducks get too close, there is a good chance they will be brutally attacked and possibly killed.

These brawny birds are probably the strongest of all geese. When approaching a nest or entering a small pen with tamed breeding birds, you can expect to be attacked. Children must be taught to keep their distance from these birds during the spring and summer months.

Canadas are strong flyers. To keep them grounded, the flight feathers of one wing must be clipped annually. Once a breeding flock has been established, they will often stay without having their wings trimmed. However, flying tame geese are prime targets for hunters and young or unmated birds will occasionally fly off with migrating wild geese.

Egyptian

Description — The high-stepping Egyptian is the smallest and brightest colored of all standard breeds of geese, and is kept almost exclusively for decoration. Their excellent foraging ability, low feed consumption, pretty plumage and intriguing courtship rituals make them an economical and fascinating bird for the hobbyist. Despite their name, they are not a true goose, and are grouped with the shelducks by most ornithologists.

Nearly every feature of this unique species differs from those of the breeds already described. The short bill is flattened, and at its base there is a fleshy nub that is slightly larger on males than on females. The head blends smoothly into the neck which is held vertically when the bird is alert. Long and flattened, the

Colored Egyptians are the smallest and only standardized breed of geese displaying iridescence in their plumage. Owned by Bernard Lind, Umatilla, Oregon.

small, muscular body is supported by lanky legs. The powerful wings are long and broad. The blunt wrist knob on the leading edge of each wing is better developed than on other geese. When fighting or being caught, Egyptians beat their opponent with these hard, blunt weapons, unless the wings are restrained. These wing spurs are not sharp, but being flogged with them is unpleasant and can result in painful bruises.

While the intricate color scheme of the Egyptian is attractive, it is also difficult to accurately describe. Two features that catch one's attention are the unusual pink or reddish purple bill and the bright golden-yellow or orange eyes. Rich chestnut-brown feathers border the bill, form a large circular patch around each eye and encircle the neck. The remaining areas of the head and upper neck are various shades of grayish fawn, while the lower neck and breast are smoky buff with the underbody shading into predominantly gray. On the center of the lower breast, there is a well-defined chestnut-red patch. The upper body is primarily grayish brown and lustrous reddish brown, with the lower back and tail being glossy black. The flights and outer wing are black, while the secondaries are iridescent greenish black. The forewings are pure white except for a bold black stripe running through the greater coverts. Feet and shanks vary from light pink to reddish orange. Juveniles have dull plumage, faint eye patches and no chest spot.

A white variety has been developed as a sport from normal-colored stock by waterfowl specialists. These birds are apparently partial albinos and genetically seem to be recessive to colored Egyptians. From a distance they appear all white, except for dark tails, primaries and secondaries. Upon closer examination, the eye patches and breast spot can be distinguished and it becomes apparent that the entire plumage, except for the snow-white forewings, is a pale smoky-white.

The rare White Egyptian was developed as a sport from colored stock. This pair is owned by Bud Butcher, Canby, Oregon.

Selecting Breeders — Look for mature birds with brilliant plumage, well-defined markings and trim, slender bodies. Avoid breeding from stock that has dull colors, small or irregular eye and breast patches, or oversized bodies.

Comments — Egyptians are extremely territorial and fearless during the breeding season, and in most circumstances should be penned away from all other livestock while nesting and brooding young goslings. For their size, they are probably the strongest of all domestic or semidomestic poultry, and any man, bird or beast that makes the mistake of getting too close to their nest or young are usually attacked with conviction. While Egyptians will injure or even kill other birds that invade their territory during the breeding season, throughout the rest of the year they usually get along well with most birds if not overcrowded. Egyptians mate in pairs, and often do not reproduce until their third year.

LUXURY AIR LINER

CHAPTER 6

Acquiring Stock

Once you have chosen the breed you wish to raise, suitable stock will need to be located. The importance of starting with quality birds should not be underestimated. The liveability, growth rate, egg production, body size and temperament of geese within the same variety differ considerably from one strain to another. Healthy and productive birds are necessary for your goose venture to be practical and free of needless hassles.

HATCHING EGGS

If you're adventuresome, you may want to start your flock by purchasing hatching eggs, which usually sell for one-third to one-half the price of day-old goslings. This method can be risky since eggs vary in their fertility, they may be internally damaged if shipped, and it is impossible to know just how many birds will hatch. However, in my experience of shipping and receiving thousands of eggs from most types of poultry, fresh, properly packaged goose eggs seem easier to ship safely than smaller eggs.

Ordering and Receiving Eggs by Mail

When ordering from an out-of-area source, try to make sure you are purchasing eggs from a breeder who knows how to package hatching eggs for shipping and who will not send old eggs or a high percentage of eggs from yearling geese. Shipped goose eggs out of yearling stock normally hatch poorly.

One secret to hatching shipped eggs is getting them as quickly as possible after they leave the producer. When placing your order, be sure to include your phone number, or that of a neighbor or friend, and instruct the shipper to include it on the package of eggs. If you live on a long rural route and know the approximate arrival date of the eggs, ask your postmaster to hold the eggs at the post office and phone you so the package can be picked up promptly. Hatchability can be drastically reduced if eggs are jostled around in a warm postal carrier's vehicle for most of the day.

Upon receiving a shipment of eggs that were shipped C.O.D., open the package in the presence of the postal carrier to check for breakage and count the number of eggs received. If a substantial number are broken or missing, immediately file a claim report.

Care of Shipped Eggs

Unless you know the eggs are over fourteen days old when they arrive, some breeders feel that better results can be obtained if shipped eggs are allowed to rest for six to twelve hours at 55° to 65° F (13° to 18° C) prior to being placed in the incubator or under a hen. For several hours before being set, they should be allowed to warm up to a room temperature of 70° to 80° F (21° to 27° C). Older eggs are best set promptly upon their arrival.

DAY-OLD GOSLINGS

The most common way to get started is to buy goslings. Day-olds are more readily available than either hatching eggs or adult birds, and are sturdy enough that they can be shipped from coast to coast with excellent results. Occasionally goslings are sold sexed, but normally are available only straight run. Theoretically, unsexed birds run half ganders and half geese. Practically, you may end up with considerably more males or females when purchasing goslings in small quantities.

Ordering and Receiving Goslings by Mail

When ordering goslings, instruct the shipper to include your telephone number (or, if you don't have a phone, give a neighbor's) on the shipping label. Then ask your postmaster to hold your goslings at the post office and call you upon their arrival so you can pick them up promptly. If the shipment was C.O.D. or insured, open the box in the presence of a postal employee and check the number and condition of the goslings. Should the number of live birds be significantly less than you paid for, file a claim report supplied by the post office.

Care of Shipped Goslings

The first twenty-four hours after goslings arrive are critical. The birds should be given lukewarm drinking water, food, warmth and rest as soon as possible. As the little ones are taken from the shipping carton and placed in a pre-warmed brooder, dip each of their bills in the water to help them locate

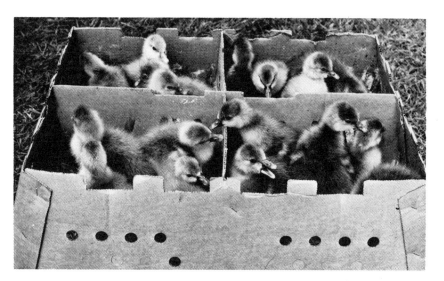

Day-old goslings ship well, normally arriving hale and hardy even after spending a couple of days in transit.

the drinking fountain. Be sure to use waterers that the goslings cannot enter, otherwise they are likely to drown or become soaked and chilled. An excellent first food that seems to perk up shipped goslings is succulent grass or clover that has been chopped into ¼- to ½-inch lengths. Goslings should be checked frequently the first couple of days, but do not handle or disturb them more than necessary until they're off to a good start.

MATURE STOCK

If you do not have the time, equipment or desire to hatch eggs or brood goslings, mature geese are often available in late summer or fall from poultry farms or hobbyists. For best productivity, birds one to three years of age are desirable, although older specimens can sometimes be had for a lower price and often will reproduce for a good number of years if they have not been abused.

Ordering and Receiving Mature Geese

Presently, adult birds can only be shipped by air freight, and they must be picked up at the nearest large airport. When placing an order for mature geese, include your phone number and that of a friend or neighbor, and instruct the shipper to put both numbers on the crates. Most air freight offices are busy. If, when your birds arrive they can't reach someone after the first several calls, they may get sidetracked and not get back to you for a number of hours or even until the following day.

Care of Shipped Geese

Mature geese can be shipped without food or water and be in transit for several days without apparent ill effect. However, they should be given water and food (grass is a good fast-breaker) as soon as possible after their arrival. So that new arrivals do not waste any of their already depleted energy through fighting, it is advisable to pen shipped birds away from your other geese for a day or two.

LOCAL OR OUT-OF-AREA?

When possible, it is advantageous to acquire geese locally since you'll save on transportation costs and the birds will be seen at the time of purchase. If a problem arises at a later date, communicating with the seller will be convenient. However, waterfowl adapt quickly to new climates and are readily shipped long distances, so you can order from out-of-area breeders and hatcheries with confidence if the birds you want are not locally available.

WHERE TO LOOK FOR STOCK

Some good places to look for sources of geese include: the Goose Breeders and Hatchery Guide in Appendix H of this book; feed stores; agriculture fairs; university poultry or animal science departments; agriculture extension services; classified ad sections of poultry, farm and garden magazines; and local newspapers.

WHAT IS A REASONABLE PRICE?

Because geese are birds, people sometimes expect to acquire them for next to nothing. However, buying a goose is more akin to purchasing a goat or a sheep than a chicken. Because of their large size, longevity and relatively low reproduction rate, geese are the highest priced of common poultry species. While price tags vary considerably, hatching eggs, goslings and mature geese generally cost — and are worth — four to six times as much as their chicken counterparts.

CHAPTER 7

Incubation

Few of nature's processes are more intriguing than the incubation of eggs. Because of their enormous size and heavy-duty shells, the hatching of goose eggs holds a special mystique and fascination for many folks. It is also true that the eggs of these dignified waterfowl have a reputation for being difficult to hatch — especially artificially. Even so, by utilizing current knowledge, satisfactory hatching results can be obtained in both small and large incubators.

HATCHING EGG CARE

Proper care of eggs prior to setting is every bit as important as correct incubation procedures. I have found that this fact is often overlooked by home flock owners. If high percentage hatches are desired, you must remember that no matter how faithfully the setting goose or foster hen sticks to her chores, or how diligently the incubator is regulated, a poor hatch will be the result if embryos have been weakened or destroyed before incubation commences.

Nests

Preincubation care of eggs begins with the right number and kind of nests. Untold numbers of goose eggs are ruined simply because adequate nests are not provided for the breeding birds. Suitable nests that are lavishly furnished with clean nesting materials protect eggs from breakage, soiling and temperature extremes. (For details on nests, see Nests, Chapter 9.)

Gathering

When eggs are going to be incubated artificially or by a foster mother, they should be picked up daily (more often during cold or hot weather) to protect them from predators and extended exposure to the elements. Always remember to handle hatching eggs gently so that the tiny embryos, which are present in newy laid eggs, are not injured or the shells cracked. Rolling eggs over repeatedly, jolting them sharply or handling them with dirty hands can decrease hatchability.

Cleaning

While nest clean eggs give the best hatching results, during damp weather they can be difficult to produce. Bits of dried dirt or straw adhering to shells can be removed with sandpaper or steel wool. Badly soiled eggs should be washed as soon as possible after gathering (within two or three hours after being laid, to be effective) to reduce the numbers of bacteria invading the egg's interior through the shell pores.

Washing does remove the cuticle (a protective film on the shell that reduces dehydration), making it necessary to raise the humidity level during incubation by approximately 5 to 10 percent. If incorrectly done, washing can drastically lower hatchability. Nonetheless, dirty eggs that have been properly washed and sanitized result in a much cleaner environment within the incubator, reduce exploding eggs and minimize infected navels in newly hatched goslings.

When eggs are washed, it is imperative that clean water, 10° to 25° F (6° to 14° C) warmer than the eggs is used. Washing with fouled water spreads contaminants from egg to egg, while cold water causes filth to be pulled deeper into the shell pores. A hatching egg sanitizer should be used in the wash water or else eggs should be washed under running water.

Selecting

Eggs that are going to be hatched should have strong, normal shells and be average to large in size. Extremely large eggs often have double yolks and seldom hatch, while small ones produce undersized, weak goslings. Cracked or irregularly shaped eggs are better suited for eating than hatching. Valuable eggs with small, tight cracks occasionally will hatch if sealed by rubbing wax or placing tape across the fracture.

(Note: it is common — although there are exceptions — for the first six to eight eggs laid by year-old geese to hatch poorly so you may not want to bother setting them. However, eggs produced during the latter part of the season often hatch reasonably well, especially if yearling breeders were well-fed throughout their first year of life.)

Storage

Where — Store hatching eggs in a cool, humid location away from direct sunlight. Cellars and basements are usually good places, while refrigerators are too cold.

Position — The position eggs are held in prior to incubation seems to have negligible effect on hatchability. A study that involved thousands of waterfowl eggs revealed no significant variation in the hatchability of eggs stored vertically with the air cell up, vertically with the air cell down or on their sides.

Temperature — If eggs are held for ten days or less, the ideal storage temperature appears to be 55° to 65° F (13° to 18° C). A slightly lower temperature of 48° to 52° F (9° to 11° C) often improves the hatchability of eggs kept over ten days. It is best to store eggs where the temperature remains constant since wide temperature fluctuations will lower the vitality of embryos.

Humidity — One of the primary concerns throughout the holding period is preventing eggs from dehydrating excessively. During dry weather, moisture loss can be curtailed by placing eggs in a covered box that is lined with three to six inches of clean bedding that has been slightly dampened — but not wet. Another excellent method is to seal boxed eggs in plastic bags from the day they are laid until setting time. When eggs are placed in plastic bags, it is vital that their shells are completely dry and that they do not touch the plastic.

Turning — Shifting goose eggs during the storage period does little to improve the hatchability of eggs held seven days or less. However, eggs that are kept more than seven days, normally hatch better if turned daily during the holding period. When eggs are stored on flats (those for turkeys are best), they can be turned by leaning one end of the container against a wall or on a block at an angle of 30° to 40°, each day alternating the end that is raised.

Length of Storage — As a rule, the shorter the holding period, the better the hatch. For consistently good hatches it is normally recommended to store eggs no more than seven to ten days prior to setting them. However, with correct storage, eggs from robust, properly fed breeding stock can often by held for two weeks with satisfactory results.

DURATION OF INCUBATION PERIOD

The typical incubation period for goose eggs is twenty-nine to thirty-one days. However, there can be considerable variation, depending on factors such as method of incubation, the breed of geese, age and diet of breeding stock and climatic temperature. For example, Pilgrims, when allowed to set on their own eggs, normally bring off broods in twenty-eight to twenty-nine days. In the opposite extreme, artificially incubated Pilgrim eggs have been known to hatch as late as the thirty-third day. Premature hatches can be brought on by high temperatures during storage and/or incubation, late hatches by long storage and low incubation temperatures. The greatest number and strongest goslings are produced when they hatch on time — which for most breeds is twenty-nine to thirty days.

AVERAGE FERTILITY

One can't expect all eggs in a large setting to be fertile. The average fertility for light and mediumweight breeds is in the range of 75 to 95 percent, and 60 to 90 percent for heavyweights. When kept in small breeding flocks of a dozen birds or less, all breeds normally have better fertility than when kept in large flocks.

Fertility normally is adversely affected by unseasonably cold or warm weather. Within one to two weeks following a sudden hot spell, fertility can fall to near zero percent — especially in Embdens. Day length also affects fertility. A minimum of twelve to thirteen hours of light per twenty-four hour period is usually required for ganders to provide good fertility. Because swimming water stimulates sexual activity in geese, the presence of bathing water — even if only six to eight inches deep — often is found to improve fertility. (See Table 8 for common causes of poor fertility.)

AVERAGE HATCHABILITY

Artificially incubated goose eggs have the lowest hatchability of all poultry eggs. However, it is not unusual for a setting goose to hatch every fertile egg. Under artificial incubation, the average hatchability falls between 55 to 75 percent of all eggs set, or 65 to 85 percent of the fertile eggs.

The diet of breeding geese and the hatchability of their eggs are closely linked. Excessive amounts of calcium can produce heavy-shelled eggs that are difficult for the goslings to penetrate, while deficiencies in protein and certain vitamins and minerals can result in embryos too weak to hatch. (See Chapter 9 for feeding of breeding geese and Table 8 for other causes of poor hatchability.)

NATURAL INCUBATION

Frequently, the most sensible method for hatching a modest number of goslings is natural incubation. A setting goose supplies the precise temperature and instinctively knows just how often her eggs need to be turned.

Choosing Natural Mothers

The Breed Profile Chart, Table 6, indicates the average mothering ability of the various breeds. If you do not have a goose for setting, ducks (Muscovies are especially well adapted), turkeys except large Broadbreasted Bronze and Whites which are too heavy) and chicken hens can be employed for incubation chores.

Clutch Size

Geese usually can handle six to twelve of their own eggs. Females, especially of the Chinese breed, sometimes lay such large clutches that they cannot properly incubate the eggs. To prevent a total loss, the oldest eggs —

those that are the dirtiest — should be removed, leaving only the quantity that the goose can cover comfortably. Depending on the weather and size of the eggs, medium to large duck and chicken hens can be entrusted with four to six goose eggs, Muscovies five to seven and turkeys eight to twelve. Fewer eggs can be incubated properly in cold weather than in warm. For eggs to hatch well, they must be positioned in a single layer — never stack them on top of each other. Too many eggs in a nest will produce only a poor hatch at best.

Care of the Broody Hen

Setting hens of all species are temperamental and should not be bothered by people or animals. Isolating the broody from the remainder of the flock with a temporary partition is beneficial. This safeguard will prevent other birds from using the broody's nest and disrupting the incubation proceedings. If attempted early, geese and their nests can sometimes be moved short distances, but this practice is risky.

A setting goose or foster hen must have a balanced diet, clean drinking water and protection from predators if she is to stay healthy during her nesting chores. Geese often nest in the open, and if a shelter for shade is not provided, they can die of sunstroke or be driven off the nest by the heat. Feed and water containers should be located at least several feet from the nest so the female must get off to eat and drink. A leave of absence from the nest for ten to fifteen minutes once or twice daily is essential to the hen's good health and will not harm the eggs.

When geese or ducks are employed to hatch goose eggs, it is beneficial for them to have bathing water, which reduces the occurence of mites and lice and provides moisture for the eggs. If a pond or stream is not available, then a tank, child's wading pool or even a dishpan will suffice.

Special Precautions with Chicken and Turkey Hens

When chicken and turkey hens are used to hatch goose eggs, they should be treated for lice and mites several days before their setting chores commence. These parasites kill and drive more hens off their nests than any other single factor, and they can bring quick death to newly hatched goslings. While some chickens turn goose eggs sufficiently, other don't. It is a good practice to mark the eggs with an X and O on opposite sides and hand turn them twice daily. Unless the nests are located on damp ground, goose eggs incubated by foster hens often hatch better if the eggs and nest are sprinkled with warm (110° to 120° F, 43° to 49° C) water daily from the fifth to twenty-seventh day of incubation.

Nests for Setting Geese and Foster Hens

Proper nests are often overlooked, but are very important for consistently satisfactory hatches. Good nests provide protection from the blazing sun and hard rains, and should be sufficiently insulated with nesting material to keep eggs clean and retain warmth. To prevent eggs from dehydrating excessively, nests used for setting should be placed directly on damp soil. When nests with solid bottoms are used or during warm, dry weather, adding several large handfuls of fresh green grass clippings to nests two or three times during the incubation period is an aid in maintaining adequate humidity. (See Chapter 9 for descriptions of nests).

ARTIFICIAL INCUBATION

Even though natural incubation is simple and efficient, there are times when incubators are necessary. Incubators can be used any season of the year, and come in such a wide range of sizes that any number of eggs — from one to thousands — can be set simultaneously or on alternate dates. However, there are some disadvantages in using mechanical mothers. Generally, the hatchability is lowered and the quantity of weak or crippled young increased when artificially hatched. Machines also need to be checked regularly to be sure the temperature, humidity and ventilation are correct and to turn the eggs if it's not done automatically. Also, electric incubators are at the mercy of power failures unless a gasoline generator is available during emergencies.

Types of Incubators

Incubators are available in a variety of sizes and shapes with differing levels of automation. They can be categorized into two basic types: still-air (gravity flow) and forced-air. Either type can be used for hatching goose eggs.

Still-Air — These incubators resemble natural incubation since the heat source is located above a single layer of eggs, making the top of the eggs warmer than the bottom. Still-air machines are dependable, easy to operate, nearly maintenance-free, moderately priced, have capacities of 25 to 170 goose eggs and are available with oil or electric heat. We have tested four still-air models and have had satisfactory results with each. For many small flock owners, I consider this type to be the most practical.

Forced-Air — These models, usually with multiple layers of eggs, have fans or beaters to circulate the warmed air around each egg. Forced-air machines are available with capacities of less than a hundred to many thousands of eggs, and when compared to still-air incubators, are better suited to automatic turning of eggs and take less floor space for larger quantities of eggs. They are also more complicated, require greater maintenance and sell for higher prices than their still-air counterparts.

Homemade Incubators

With a little imagination and lots of perserverance, satisfactory hatches can be obtained in a homemade incubator consisting of a cardboard or wooden box and light bulbs for heat. A deluxe model, complete with heating element and thermostat, can also be crafted in the home shop. (Kits for making small incubators are manufactured by the Lyon Electric Company. See Appendix I for their address.) In emergency situations — such as a bird deserting her nest near

Several popular incubators used by home flock owners

clear plastic forced-air model
with a capacity for 7 to 9 eggs

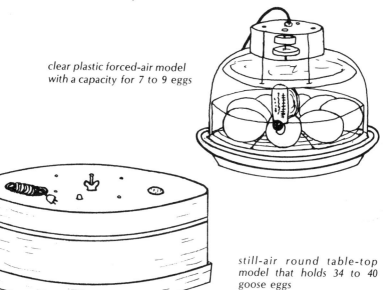

still-air round table-top
model that holds 34 to 40
goose eggs

cabinet type forced-
air machine available
with goose egg
capacities of 160 and
up

the end of the incubation period — frying pans or heating pads have been used to hatch eggs.

Where to Place the Incubator

Incubators perform their best in rooms or buildings where the temperature does not fluctuate more than 5° to 10° F (3° to 5° C) over a twenty-four hour period. Consistent temperatures are especially important for still-air incubators, which should be located in a room with an average temperature not lower than 60° to 70° F (16° to 21° C). Do not position your machine where it will be in direct sunlight, or near a window, heater or air conditioner.

Leveling the Incubator

Incubators, especially still-air models, need to be level to operate correctly. If operated while setting askew, the surface area of the water pans will be changed and the temperature of the eggs will vary in different areas of the machine, causing eggs to hatch poorly and over an extended period of time.

Operating Specifications

Manufacturers of incubators include a manual of operating instructions with their machines. This guide should be carefully read and followed. The operating instructions often cannot be adapted from one machine to another with good results, particularly if one is a still-air model and the other a forced-air. If you acquire a used incubator which does not have an instruction booklet, manufacturers are usually willing to send a new manual if you send them a request with the model number of your machine.

Setting the Eggs — Start the incubator at least forty-eight to seventy-two hours ahead of time, making all necessary adjustments of temperature, humidity and ventilation before the eggs are set. People frequently put eggs in machines that are not properly regulated, thinking they can make fine adjustments after the eggs are in place. This practice is a serious mistake that can kill or weaken the embryo, since one of the most critical periods is the first few days of incubation.

Prior to setting, goose eggs need to be warmed gradually for five to six hours to a room temperature of 70° to 85° F (21° to 29° C) or, if possible, placed on top of the incubator. If cold eggs are taken directly from storage and set without this warming period, water condenses on the shells, and yolks occasionally rupture.

For high percentage hatches, it is important that goose eggs be incubated with the large end (air cell) at least slightly raised. If set with the air cell lowered, there is an increased possibility that the embryos will be malpositioned at hatching time with the heads away from the air cell, thus reducing their chances of hatching unassisted. Never crowd or stack eggs on top of each other, but set only those that fit comfortably on the tray. If at all possible, do not disturb eggs during the first twenty-four hours they are in the incubator.

Temperature — It is always wise to use thermometers designed for incubators, as they have greater accuracy than utility models and normally are easier to read. Also, thermometers with temperature scales etched directly on the glass are preferred to those that are stapled to a marked backing, since this backing can slide, giving an inaccurate reading. Prior to each hatching season, it is a good idea to test the accuracy of incubator thermometers by placing them in lukewarm water along with an oral fever thermometer.

Generally, temperature recommendations for goose eggs are slightly lower than those for chicken eggs. The correct thermometer reading in incubators varies according to the type of machine being used and climatic temperature. In forced-air machines, temperatures of 99.25° to 99.5° F (37.3° to 37.5° C) are normally recommended in cool weather, while 99° F (37.2° C) is usually adequate once the weather is consistently warm. Still-air incubators must be maintained several degrees warmer at 101.5° to 102.5° F (38.6° to 39.2° C) since only the tops of the eggs are warmed.

It is essential that thermometers be positioned properly in still-air incubators or an incorrect temperature reading will be given. The top of the thermometer's bulb must be level with the top of the eggs. Do not lay the thermometer on top of the eggs since this practice will give a warmer temperature reading than actually exists at the level of the eggs, plus the eggs under the thermometer will be shielded from the warmth.

During the last seven to ten days of incubation the heat should be closely watched since an increase in temperature is often experienced, especially in small machines. The thermostat may need to be adjusted daily during this period to keep the eggs from overheating. Some hatchery operators feel that lowering the temperature by 1° to 2° F (.5° to 1° C) after the twenty-seventh day is beneficial since goslings generate considerable internal heat in their struggle to free themselves from their shells, and cooler temperatures seem to stimulate the hatching birds.

Humidity — To have a large number of strong goslings hatch, the contents of the eggs must gradually dehydrate the correct amount. When dehydration is excessive, the embryos are puny, weak and sticky, making it extra tough for them to break out of the eggs. Conversely, inadequate moisture loss results in chubby embryos that have difficulty turning within the egg and cracking all the way around the shell.

The amount of moisture in the air inside the incubator determines the dehydration rate of the eggs. Moisture is usually supplied by water evaporation pans. To control humidity, the water surface area is increased or decreased, and the amount of ventilation regulated.

If your incubator is equipped with a wet-bulb thermometer or hygrometer, the correct reading on these instruments typically is between 84° to 88° F (29° to 31° C), which is equal to a relative humidity of approximately 55 to 62 percent. When eggs have been washed prior to incubation, the above figures may need to be raised to 88° to 90° F (31° to 32° C) on the wet-bulb thermometer or 65 percent on the hygrometer. Throughout the hatch (the last three days of incubation), the relative humidity should be increased to approximately 75 percent, or 90° to 93° F (32° to 33.9° C) on the wet-bulb thermometer.

While the hygrometer is a useful instrument for measuring the humidity level in incubators, the best indicators of whether the contents of the eggs are dehydrating at the correct rate are weight loss (which should be about 2.5 percent per week) and/or size of air cells. The air cell's volume can be observed by candling the eggs. On the seventh, fourteenth, twenty-first and twenty-sixth days of incubation, the average air cell volume should be approximately the same size as those in the accompanying illustration. If the air cells or weight loss are too large, increase the moisture in the incubator by adding more water surface and/or decrease the amount of ventilation, being careful not to reduce the airflow so severely as to suffocate the embryos. If on the other hand, the air cells are too small, decrease the water surface and/or increase ventilation.

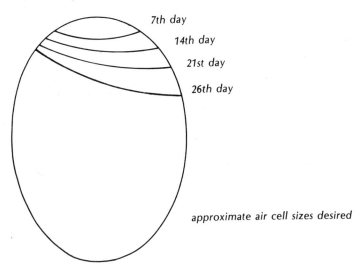

7th day

14th day

21st day

26th day

approximate air cell sizes desired

Due to variations in egg size and shell quality, humidity requirements can vary significantly among eggs produced not only by different breeds, but also by individual geese. Large eggs dehydrate slower than small ones. When eggs of different sizes and from various breeds are incubated together, it is often found that some eggs will dehydrate properly while others dry down excessively or not enough.

Ventilation — The developing embryo needs a constant supply of fresh air, which is provided through vent openings usually located in the sides and tops of incubators. The amount of ventilation required is relatively small, but is essential to the well-being of the imprisoned goslings. Ventilation demands are greater at hatching time with the increased activities, but adjustable air vents must not be opened excessively or too much moisture will be lost. When using an incubator that is not specifically designed for hatching goose eggs, it can be difficult to provide sufficient air turnover while at the same time maintaining adequate humidity, particularly if you're located in a dry climate.

Turning — Incubating eggs must be turned to exercise the embryos and keep them from sticking to the shell membrane. A few eggs may hatch if you turn them just once or twice every twenty-four hours, but turning three to five times daily at regular intervals is the minimum for high percentage hatches. For best results, goose eggs need to be rotated 180° at each turning, unless they are turned automatically every hour, when a one-third revolution is satisfactory. Irregular or rough turning can be disastrous for goose eggs. Manual turning should begin twenty-four to thirty-six hours after the eggs are set, while automatic turning can commence immediately. Both should be discontinued three days before the scheduled hatch date or when the first egg is pipped, whichever comes first.

When turning eggs manually, mark them with an X on one side and an O on the other. Always use a wax or lead pencil, never liquid inks — such as a felt tip — since they clog shell pores and can poison the embryo. After each turning, all eggs should have the same mark facing up.

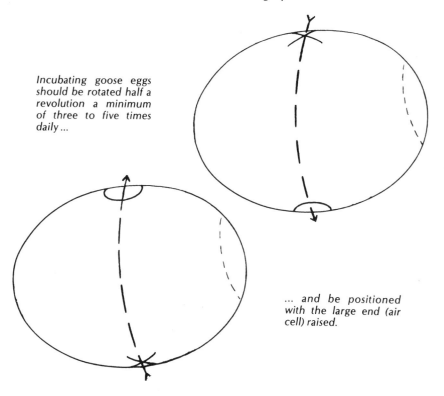

Incubating goose eggs should be rotated half a revolution a minimum of three to five times daily ...

... and be positioned with the large end (air cell) raised.

Cooling — For best results when using still-air incubators, goose eggs should be cooled once daily — except during the first week and last three days of incubation. (Satisfactory hatches are usually obtained in forced-air machines without cooling.) When the room temperature is 70° F (21° C), goose eggs should be cooled five to seven minutes a day the second week, eight to ten minutes daily the third week, and twelve to fifteen minutes the first three or four days of the fourth week.

While goose eggs may hatch if left without heat for up to twelve hours once or twice during incubation (except during the first week and the last five days when low temperatures are disastrous), repeated overcooling will retard growth and can be fatal. Using a kitchen timer and setting it as a reminder helps avoid this costly mistake. If you ever discover the incubator overheated by more than 2° F (1° C), cool the eggs immediately for ten to fiteen minutes and correct the problem.

Sprinkling and Dipping — Most experienced waterfowl breeders and hatchery operators agree that artificially incubated goose eggs normally hatch better if they are periodically sprayed with or dipped in lukewarm (110° F, 43° C) water. What is not always agreed upon is how often and why watering these eggs is beneficial. Some believe that wetting goose eggs softens the shell and prevents the contents from dehydrating excessively. Others feel that a major benefit is that as the water evaporates from the shell, the egg is cooled, stimulating and strengthening the embryo.

While you may want to experiment to see what works best for you, I have had consistently good results by spraying goose eggs with warm water either once daily or every other day from the seventh to twenty-eighth day of incubation. To prevent the egg membranes from drying out and becoming tough during the hatch, it is sometimes necessary — especially in dry weather or in incubators not designed for these large eggs — to spray or sprinkle goose eggs daily after the first eggs are pipped. A convenient method for wetting eggs is to use a well-cleaned hand spray bottle sold at garden centers. Dipping for several seconds is okay for small numbers of eggs.

CANDLING

Goose eggs can be safely candled to check fertility by the seventh day of incubation. Candling prematurely increases the possibility of accidentally discarding fertile eggs.

Eggs are candled in a darkened room with an egg candler or flashlight. By the seventh day, fertile eggs reveal a small dark spot with a network of blood vessels branching out from it, closely resembling a spider in the center of its web. Embryos sometimes attach themselves near the top of the egg where they are difficult to observe, so if in doubt, it's best to give the egg a second chance. Infertile eggs are clear with the yolk appearing as a floating shadow when the egg is moved from side to side.

Sometimes embryos begin to develop, and then perish after several days. If this occurs, a circle or streak of blood can often be seen in an otherwise clear egg. Rotting eggs often exhibit black spots on the inside of the shell, with darkened, cloudy areas floating in the egg's interior. All eggs not containing live embryos should be removed from the incubator. Rotting eggs give off harmful gases and frequently explode, contaminating the other eggs and the incubator's interior with a putrid smelling and bacteria-filled goo that is difficult and unpleasant to remove.

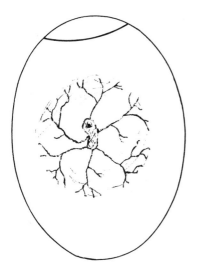 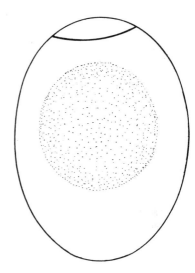

Fertile egg (left) and infertile egg (right) on the 7th day.

USES FOR INFERTILE EGGS

Goose eggs that are clear when candled after the first week of incubation can be used for the popular craft of egg decoration and are useful as a feed supplement for all types of young and mature poultry and other livestock such as pigs, cats and dogs. When feeding eggs to poultry or pets, always hard boil them and mix with other food. Uncooked eggs can cause a biotin deficiency or result in birds and animals robbing nests to satisfy their appetite for raw eggs. Contaminated eggs having cloudy contents or dark splotches on the interior are unsuitable for livestock food. Bury rotting eggs where animals and birds cannot get to them.

ROTTING AND EXPLODING EGGS

The contents of eggs will sometimes rot during the incubation period. In this condition, eggs give off foul smelling gases, and in severe cases, sufficient internal pressure develops so that the contents ooze from the shell pores or the egg explodes. Rot can occur in all types of eggs, but normally is a greater problem in waterfowl eggs. Two important contributions are that waterfowl eggs have a long incubation period and nest clean duck and goose eggs can be difficult to produce, especially if the breeding stock is kept in close confinement.

Spoilage is caused by invading organisms that reproduce at runaway rates in the congenial environment found in incubating eggs. The troublesome bacteria and other organisms normally enter through the shell pores after eggs are laid, but there is evidence that eggs can have high levels of contamination before being laid if females have infected reproductive tracts.

Keeping egg rot to a minimum is a matter of making sure eggs are not unnecessarily exposed to bacteria and other harmful organisms. Conditions that increase the possibility of contamination include filthy living quarters, bottomless or dirty nests, eggs laid on the ground, eggs that are fouled with excrement, eggs left in nests all day, handling eggs with dirty hands, storing eggs in dirty containers, improper cleaning and washing of eggs, poorly sanitized incubators and breeding stock having reproductive or digestive tract infections.

While good housekeeping procedures normally keep the rotting egg problem to a minimum, there are several other practices that can be useful. Since bacteria are present to some degree even in clean nests, some breeders routinely fumigate hatching eggs with formaldehyde gas per the specifications in Table 7. To be effective, this fumigation must take place within two or three hours after eggs are laid. If delayed, fumigation will be of little value since the bacteria will have already invaded the inner egg where the fumigant cannot reach. Fumigation of soiled eggs is futile since organic matter neutralizes the formaldehyde gas.

Because it can be difficult to get hatching eggs fumigated within the short effective period after they are laid, a dry powder form of formaldehyde (Formaldagen F., by Vineland Laboratories) has been developed which is used directly in the nests at the rate of approximately one ounce per nest. The body heat from the laying bird triggers the release of formaldehyde gas, fumigating the egg at laying time. This product is reported to be effective if used in dry, clean nests and in conjunction with good management.

Another means of reducing the numbers of harmful organisms on hatching eggs is to submerge them in a dip containing an approved hatching egg sanitizer (check with your feed or poultry supply dealers) and then air dried. Again, this method is effective only if the eggs are reasonably clean and it is carried out within a couple hours after the eggs are laid.

THE HATCH

After four weeks of fussing over a setting of eggs and daily trying to visualize what's happening within the heavy calcium walls, those first muffled chirps telling that the hatch is near are tonic for the human spirit. And if one listens carefully, especially when using a still-air incubator that's off in a quiet nook, it's possible to hear and even feel the thick shells crack and pop as the struggling goslings fight for their new life.

If your incubator is filled to capacity and has adjustable air vents, regulate these ports to allow additional air for the hatching goslings. However, do not open them so wide that an excessive amount of warm, moist air escapes and the humidity drops. In order to maintain adequate humidity along with the increased air circulation during the hatch, you may find it necessary to place extra water containers in the machine or place a flannel or terrycloth wick in the water pan, running the cloth along the edge of the tray. To keep humid air from escaping, resist your curiosity and leave the machine closed for as long as the water supply lasts. Fill pans on the twenty-eighth day with 100° F (37.8° C) water and, if possible, do not reopen until the thirtieth day — when the hatch

The reward of proper incubation is strong, healthy goslings.

should be complete. Be sure and cover the water pans with screen or hardware cloth to prevent goslings from entering and drowning.

Goslings often begin pipping their eggs as early as seventy-two hours prior to the hatch date. They usually require one to two and a half days to completely rim the shell and exit. Newly hatched birds are wet and exhausted, and should remain unmolested in the incubator six to twenty-four hours while drying off and gaining strength.

Removing Goslings from the Incubator

If the trays are crowded, goslings and empty shells should be removed when the hatch is half completed in order to give the remaining eggs more room. Before opening the machine, have a clean container — with sides no less than six inches high — prepared with soft bedding, such as old rags. While transferring the goslings, work quickly but gently, discarding empty shells and pipped eggs containing birds that are obviously dead. During this operation, the room temperature should not be below 60° F (16° C), with 70° to 80° F (21° to 27° C) being preferred. Have a spray bottle filled with warm water handy so that just before closing the machine again, the remaining eggs can be sprayed to replace moisture lost while the incubator was open. Getting a little water on goslings left in the machine will not harm them.

Help-Outs

At the end of the hatch there often remain a number of live goslings which are still imprisoned within partially opened shells. Most of us find it hard to ig-nore these and wish to help them out. Assistance can be given by breaking away just enough shell to allow the bird to emerge by itself. If bleeding occurs during this operation, stop immediately, as the bird's circulatory system is still attached to the inner lining of the shell and the yolk sac is probably not totally absorbed into the abdomen.

While some birds which are assisted from the shell develop into fine specimens, a large percentage are usually handicapped by a deformity or weakness. When it is understood that the hatch is a fitness test given by nature to cull out the weak and deformed — protecting them from facing a life for which they are ill prepared — we can take a more realistic view of helping goslings from the shell.

It is advantageous to mark all help-outs so they are not used as breeders unless they exhibit exceptional vigor and strength as mature birds. Indiscriminate use of these goslings for breeding can lower the vitality and hatchability of subsequent generations.

INCUBATOR SANITATION

While the incubator supplies the correct conditions for the embryo to develop, it also provides an excellent environment for the rapid growth of molds and bacteria. Consequently, it is essential that the incubator be kept as clean as possible. At the conclusion of each hatch, you should clean and disinfect the incubator. Sunlight has excellent sanitizing powers. When feasible, it is a good idea to place small machines or trays from larger incubators out in the midday sun for several hours. If eggs are set to hatch at various times, the water pans should be emptied, cleaned and returned with warm water, and the gosling fuzz removed from the incubator with a damp cloth or vacuum cleaner. At the end of the hatching season, thoroughly clean and air-out the incubator and store it in a dry, sanitary location.

FUMIGATION

On the average homestead, fumigation normally is not required for satisfactory hatching results. However, when large numbers of eggs are set and hatched continuously over a period of time and the incubator cannot be thoroughly cleaned and disinfected between each hatch, the bacteria count within the machine will soar, resulting in reduced hatchability of the eggs and diminished liveability of the goslings that are produced. When continuous setting and hatching of eggs is practiced, a sound fumigation schedule will usually improve your results.

When to Fumigate

Table 7 gives a fumigation schedule. Of the five fumigations listed, numbers 1 and 5 are usually sufficient.

- Fumigation number 1 should be carried out in a tight cabinet that is outfitted with a fan for circulating the fumigation gas. Eggs should be placed on wire racks, in wire baskets or on clean egg flats. The sooner this

TABLE 7   FUMIGATION SCHEDULE

Type of Fumigation	Amount of Fumigant per Cubic Ft. of Air Space		Length of Time Air Vents Should be Closed	Correct Conditions for Fumigation	
	Potassium-Permanganate	Formalin (37.5%)		Minimum Air Temp.	Minimum Humidity
#1 Immediately after eggs are gathered and cleaned	.6 grams	1.2 cc	20 minutes	70° F	70%
#2 Within 16 hours after eggs are set	.4 grams	.8 cc	20 minutes	99.5° F	55%
#3 60 hours prior to end of incubation period	.4 grams	.8 cc	20 minutes	98° F	65%
#4 30 hours prior to end of incubation period	none	.5 cc	none	98° F	65%
#5 Empty incubators at beginning and end of season & between settings	.6 grams	1.2 cc	3-12 hours	99° F	55%

fumigation takes place after the eggs are laid (preferably within two hours), the more effective it will be.

- Fumigation number 2 takes place in the incubator within the first sixteen hours after the eggs are set, but not before the temperature and humidity have had a chance to normalize. Between the 24th and 120th hours of incubation, embryos go through a critical period. If eggs are exposed to formaldehyde gas during this time, the developing goslings can be weakened or killed. However, when continuous setting is practiced in the same incubator, eggs can be fumigated several times during the course of the incubation period if they are not fumigated during this critical period.

- When eggs are transferred to a separate machine for the hatch, fumigation number 3 can be employed to control outbreaks of omphalitis (a bacterial infection of the navel in newly hatched birds). To prevent damage to the lung tissue of the goslings, this fumigation needs to be performed before the eggs are pipped.

- Fumigation number 4 is normally applied only when number 3 does not control omphalitis.

- Prior to the first setting of the season, between hatches and at the end of the hatching season, fumigation number 5 should be used after incubators have been thoroughly washed and disinfected.

To be effective, a fumigation schedule should be designed and followed. Haphazard fumigating is of little value and is a waste of time and money. Under no circumstances should fumigation replace other sanitation procedures.

Procedures

The fumigation agent is formaldehyde gas which is produced by pouring liquid formalin over dry potassium-permanganate crystals. While formaldehyde gas is highly toxic, fumigation will destroy harmful bacteria and disease organisms without harming the eggs, the incubator or you, the operator, if the correct procedures are followed.

Step 1—Calculate the airspace within your incubator by multiplying the width times the depth times the height.

Step 2—Close all ventilation openings.

Step 3—Warm up the incubator until it is operating at normal temperature and humidity levels for incubation.

Step 4—Measure out the correct quantity of potassium-permanganate (as per Table 7) into a dry earthenware, enamelware or glass container — never use metallic receptacles — having a capacity at least ten times the total volume of the ingredients, and place in the incubator.

Step 5—Without leaning over the container, pour the correct amount of formalin over the potassium-permanganate and quickly shut the incubator door. The chemical reaction of these two substances begins within seconds. To prevent damage to your mucous membranes or burns on your skin, never combine these chemicals outside of the incubator or while holding the mixing vessel.

Step 6—After the correct allotment of time, open the air vents to exhaust the formaldehyde gas. Thirty minutes to several hours later, remove the fumigation container and dispose of the residue in a safe location where children or animals cannot get into it.

A Word of Caution

Formaldehyde gas is toxic to small and large organisms alike. When fumigating, follow instructions carefully and do not take chances which endanger your health.

If goslings are fumigated thirty hours before the end of the incubation period (fumigation #4 in Table 7), no potassium-permanganate is used. Rather, sufficient cheesecloth is used to absorb the formalin and then hung in the incubator, allowing time for total evaporation. It is extremely important that the cloth is positioned so that it does not touch any of the eggs or restrict air circulation.

INCUBATION CHECK LIST

1. To produce clean eggs, provide adequate nests furnished with clean nesting material.

2. Gather eggs in morning to protect from temperature extremes.

3. Handle eggs with clean hands or gloves and avoid shaking, jolting or rolling them.

4. Store eggs in clean containers in a cool, humid location, and turn them daily if held longer than seven days.

5. Set only reasonably clean eggs with normal shells.

6. Start incubator well in advance of using. Make adjustments of temperature, humidity and ventilation before eggs are set.

7. When filling the incubator, always position eggs with their air cell slightly raised, and do not crowd eggs on tray.

8. If eggs are manually turned, do not disturb them during the first twenty-four hours they are in the incubator.

9. Gently turn eggs a minimum of three times daily at regular intervals from the second to twenty-fifth day.

10. Operate still-air incubators at 101.5° to 102.5° F (38.6° to 39.2° C), and forced-air machines at 99° to 99.5° F (37.2° to 37.5° C) during the incubation period.

11. Maintain relative humidity at 55 to 62 percent (a wet-bulb reading of 84° to 88° F or 29° to 31° C) for the first twenty-five days of incubation.

12. When using a still-air machine, cool eggs five to seven minutes a day the second week, eight to ten minutes daily the third week, and twelve to fiteen minutes the first four days of the fourth week.

13. Starting on the seventh day, spray or dip eggs in lukewarm (110° F or 43° C) water daily or every other day.

14. If all eggs in the machine were set at the same time or a separate hatcher is used, you may want to lower the incubation temperature 1° to 2° F (.5° to 1° C) for the hatch.

15. Increase the relative humidity to approximately 75 percent (a wet-bulb reading of 90° to 93° F or 32° to 33.9° C) for the hatch.

16. Do not open incubator except when absolutely necessary during the hatch.

17. Thoroughly clean and disinfect incubator after each hatch.

TABLE 8   PINPOINTING INCUBATION PROBLEMS

Symptoms	Common Causes	Remedies
More than 10 to 25% clear eggs when candled on the 7th to 10th day of incubation	1 Too few or too many ganders 2 Immature breeders 3 Old, crippled or fat breeders 4 Breeders frequently frightened 5 No swimming water for mating 6 No green feed during breeding season or ration lacking UGF 7 First eggs of the season 8 Medication in feed or water 9 Old eggs 10 Moldy feed or blighted grain	1 Correct gander to goose ratio 2 Use breeders 2 years or older 3 Younger, active, semi-fat breeders 4 Work calmly around breeders 5 Swimming water for large breeds 6 Lush pasture, leafy greens or other UGF containing feeds (Ch. 9) 7 Don't set eggs laid first week 8 Avoid medicating breeders 9 Set fresher eggs 10 Never use moldy feeds or blighted grains
Blood rings on 7th to 10th day	1 Faulty storage of eggs 2 Irregular incubation temperature	1 Proper storage of eggs 2 Adjust machine ahead of time
Ruptured air cell	1 Rough handling or a deformity	1 Handle and turn eggs gently
Yolk stuck to shell's interior	1 Old eggs which haven't been turned regularly during storage	1 Turn eggs daily if they are held for more than 5 days
Dark blotches on shell's interior	1 Dirt or bacteria on shells causing contamination of the inner egg	1 Wash eggs soon after gathering with water and sanitizer
More than 5% dead embryos between 7th and 25th day of incubation	1 Inadequate breeder diet 2 Highly inbred breeding stock 3 Incorrect incubation temperature 4 Periods of low or high temperature 5 Faulty turning during incubation 6 Breeder ration lacking UGF	1 Supply balanced diet 2 Introduce new birds to flock 3 Check accuracy and position of thermometer 4 Check temperature frequently; don't overcool eggs 5 Turn minimum of 3 times daily 6 Ration with UGF (see Ch. 9)
Rotting, oozing and exploding eggs during incubation	1 Bacterial infection of eggs 2 Breeders kept in filthy environment 3 Dirty nests 4 Fecal contamination of shells 5 Cross contamination 6 Infection in female reproductive tract	1 Gather eggs frequently, fumigate or dip 2-3 hours after being laid 2 Reasonably clean living quarters 3 Clean nesting material; wooden or burlap bottoms to keep eggs off ground 4 Do not set filthy eggs 5 Handle eggs with clean hands; if eggs must be washed, use clean water 10-30° F warmer than eggs, plus sanitizer 6 Uncontaminated feed, clean living quarters, antibiotics
Early hatches	1 High incubation temperatures	1 Lower incubation temperature
Late hatches	1 Low incubation temperatures 2 Eggs overcooled during incubation	1 Raise incubation temperature 2 Use timer so cooling eggs aren't forgotten
Eggs pipped in small end	1 Eggs incubated in wrong position	1 Position eggs with small end lower than the large end

TABLE 8 - continued

Eggs pip but do not hatch; many fully developed goslings dead in shells that aren't pipped	1 High humidity during incubation 2 Low humidity during incubation 3 Eggs chilled or overheated during last 5 days of incubation 4 Low humidity during the hatch causing egg membrane to dry out 5 Poor ventilation during hatch 6 Disturbances during hatch	1 Decrease amount of moisture 2 Increase amount of moisture 3 Protect eggs from temperature extremes during this critical period 4 Last 3 days, raise humidity to 75-80% and sprinkle eggs daily 5 Increase air-flow during hatch 6 Leave incubator closed
Sticky goslings	1 Probably low humidity during incubation and/or hatch	1 Increase amount of moisture
Large, protruding navels	1 High temperature 2 Excessive dehydration of eggs 3 Bacteria infection	1 Lower temperature; check thermometer 2 Increase humidity level 3 Improve sanitation practices
Dead goslings in incubator	1 Suffocation or overheating 2 Severe bacteria infection	1 Increase ventilation during the hatch and watch temperature carefully 2 Improve sanitation of hatching eggs and incubation
Spraddled legs	1 Smooth incubator trays	1 Cover trays with hardware cloth
More than 5% cripples other than spraddled legs	1 Inadequate turning during incubation 2 Prolonged periods of cooling 3 Inherited defects	1 Turn eggs a minimum of 3 times daily 2 Don't forget eggs when cooling 3 Select breeders free of defects

Sticky goslings are normally associated with improper humidity during incubation.

CHAPTER 8

Rearing Goslings

Few baby birds are more endearing or faster growing than young geese. Inquisitive, trusting and talkative from the start, newly hatched goslings are as friendly as puppies, and, when raised in small groups, some people claim they can learn to respond to individual names. Weighing a mere three to four ounces at hatching time, medium to large breed goslings that are well-fed grow into chunky ten- to twelve-pound birds in a short eight to twelve weeks.

BASIC GUIDELINES

When raising geese for the first time, persons accustomed to keeping chickens marvel at the amazing growth rate and hardiness of goslings. Along with ducklings, the young of geese are generally considered the easiest of all domestic fowl to bring up from hatching to maturity. When the following guidelines are put into practice, rearing goslings is an enjoyable and trouble-free adventure, and you'll have an excellent chance of raising every bird to adulthood.

Keep them warm and dry, and protect from drafts — Cold goslings lose their appetites, and when wet, quickly chill and die if not promptly warmed and dried. Drinking water containers that are used the first couple of weeks should be designed so the birds cannot enter and become excessively wet. Until well-feathered (five to eight weeks) young geese should be put under cover during hard rains. Chilling and drowning are two of the goslings' worst enemies.

Maintain them on wire floors or dry, mold-free bedding that provides good footing — Damp, filthy bedding is a breeding ground not only for internal parasites and disease organisms, but also for molds that cause serious respiratory disorders. Slick surfaces, such as newspapers, are the leading cause of spraddled legs.

Supply a balanced diet of fresh, non-medicated feed — To insure rapid growth and disease resistance, a proper diet is essential. Moldy or medicated feed can cause retarded growth, sickness and death. When available, supply succulent greens since grass is the natural diet of geese of all ages, and its feeding reduces the grocery bill and is an aid in preventing digestive disorders. However, grass alone is not enough and goslings should be started with feed that provides a minimum of 16 to 17 percent protein. Do not feed laying rations to immature birds since these feeds contain far too much calcium and an improper phosphorus to calcium ratio which can result in stunted growth, rickets and other bone deformities, and in acute cases, lead to death. (See Leg Problems, Chapter 11 and Phosphorus:Calcium Ratio, Appendix A.)

Provide a constant supply of fresh drinking water — Goslings do poorly if frequently left stranded without drinking water. Putrid, stagnant water is a prime source of health problems. Once goslings are a week or two old, providing water that they can submerge their heads in seems to help prevent eye infections.

Furnish adequate floorspace and fresh air — Forcing goslings to live in crowded, filthy conditions is the leading cause of cannibalism and disease.

Protect from predators — Both tame and wild meat-eating animals and birds find unprotected goslings easy prey. Following closely behind drowning, predators are the second leading cause of death in young waterfowl that are raised in small flocks.

Be calm and gentle — Goslings thrive on tranquility. If repeatedly frightened, they become nervous wrecks, grow poorly and pile up in corners, which can result in badly torn backs. To gain their confidence, move slowly and talk to young geese when working with them. Before entering a building or pen where they can't see you coming, knock or give a vocal signal that lets them know you're approaching.

NATURAL BROODING

Watching a pair of geese parenting their young is a delightful experience. And although natural brooding carries with it some inherent risks, this arrangement can be practical when only a few goslings are being raised. Geese of most breeds are devoted parents, especially when two years or older. However, some Chinese and most Dewlap Toulouse cannot be depended upon for

This Pilgrim gander keeps a watchful eye over his month-old offspring.

parental duties. Egyptians, Canadas, American Buffs, Pilgrims and other light or mediumweight breeds generally make the best natural parents. If frequently disturbed by people or animals, geese — especially large breeds such as Toulouse, Embdens and Africans — can lose a substantial number of their young by trampling on them.

Managing Geese and Their Broods

The best thing you can do for a pair of geese and their newly hatched brood is to pester them as little as possible. Your main job is to provide adequate protection from predators and rodents and to prevent young goslings from getting soaked or falling into insurmountable holes.

Since goslings may be left stranded or led through wet grass, it is advisable to confine free-roaming geese and their brood in a dry, secure building or pen the first week or two. In such a setting, the entire family will be protected from wet grass, rain, cold winds and predators, and concentrated feed can be supplied to help the little ones get off to a fast start.

Because predators can be so destructive, it is worth the time required to confine geese and their young in a secure pen or building at night until the goslings are six to ten weeks old. Tight fences, close-fitting gates and yards that are free of hiding places — such as tall grass, bushes and junk piles — can all help reduce the possibility of losses to predators.

Geese can be aggressive towards strange goslings and may injure or kill them, or on the other hand, the adults may kidnap young from other broods. Generally, it is not a good practice to confine two or more pairs together in a small yard with their broods, particularly during the first several weeks.

Using Foster Hens

Goslings can be brooded successfully by ducks, turkeys and chickens. These foster hens and their broods should be managed the same as outlined for geese, except that turkeys and chickens should always be treated for lice and mites several days before they are entrusted with goslings. To lessen the possibility of rejection, it is a good idea to slip goslings under their new parent after dark.

The number of goslings a foster hen can brood depends on her size and the weather conditions. Typically, a medium-size chicken or duck can handle six to eight goslings, bantams three to five and turkeys up to fifteen. The most important consideration is that all the goslings can be hovered and warmed at the same time.

ARTIFICIAL BROODING

Goslings adapt well to artificial brooding. The most important factors for success are that the birds be kept warm, dry, reasonably clean, and that they are protected from voracious predators. When choosing a brooding site, keep in mind that birds and animals such as rats, mink, weasels and screech owls can squeeze through openings two inches in diameter or smaller. All holes more than one-half inch across should be varmint-proofed with wire netting or can lids. Also remember that goslings can be poisoned if they are brooded on a floor that has been fouled by spilled fuel or chemical sprays and fertilizers.

The Brooder

The main function of a brooder is to provide warmth for goslings during the first three to six weeks of their life. Brooding equipment can be purchased from stores handling poultry supplies or can be fabricated at home. Fortunately, brooders do not need to be elaborate nor expensive to do an adequate job.

Homemade Brooders — If you're raising only a few goslings, during mild weather they can be brooded with an ordinary light bulb that is suspended in a box or wire cage. Colored bulbs — particularly blue — are preferred since they are the most effective in reducing feather eating and are gentler on the goslings' eyes. Be sure that the box is large enough to allow the birds to get away from direct heat when they desire.

The size of bulb required depends on the dimensions of the box and the room temperature. I suggest using several forty-watt bulbs rather than a single larger one. When using bulbs over forty watts, locate them out of the birds' reach so they don't burn themselves. Hot bulbs can be shattered if placed near the watering area where goslings splash water or by the wet tongues of curious birds. To prevent fires or the asphyxiation of goslings from smoke produced by smoldering materials, even bulbs of low wattage must not touch or be close to flammable substances.

A light reflector and clamp, available at hardware stores, make safe and practical "hover brooders." The reflector can be clamped to the side of a cage

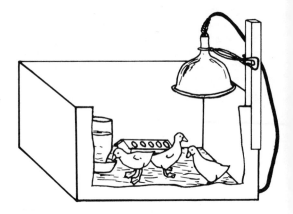

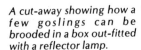

A cut-away showing how a few goslings can be brooded in a box out-fitted with a reflector lamp.

or box and will brood up to half a dozen goslings. As the young ones grow, the heat source can be adjusted to the correct height.

Infrared Heat Lamps — A simple method for brooding larger numbers of goslings is with 250-watt, infrared heat lamps with hard glass bulbs that won't break if splattered with water. Each lamp, when suspended eighteen to twenty-four inches above the litter, will provide adequate heat for fifteen to thirty goslings, depending on room temperature. It is wise to use at least two lamps in case one burns out.

Whenever heat lamps are used, extreme care must be taken to prevent fires. Goslings have been known to push straw bedding into a pile under a heat lamp, causing a fire. Always make sure lamps are suspended securely and never hang them with the bottom of the bulb closer than eighteen inches from the litter, or so that any part of the bulb is near flammable materials, such as wood or cardboard.

Heat lamps with draft guard

Hover Brooders — Available with gas, oil or electric heat, this type of brooder consists of a thermostatically controlled heater which is covered with a canopy. The brooder is supported with adjustable legs or suspended from the ceiling with a rope and easily regulated to the proper height as the birds grow. Water fountains and feeders are placed around the outside of the canopy where the goslings drink, eat and exercise in cooler temperatures. Hover brooders are available in sizes which are rated at 100 to 1000 chick capacity. The number of goslings under each unit should be limited to approximately 40 percent of the given capacity for chicks.

Battery Brooders — This kind of brooder is an all-metal cage which is equipped with a wire floor, removable dropping pan, thermostat, electric heating element, and feed and water troughs. They can be purchased and used in individual units or stacked on top of one another. Battery brooders are commonly used for starting chicks, but can also be used for brooding goslings for the first week or two. Most models have floors that are made from wire with ½-inch openings. Newly hatched goslings sometimes get their hocks caught in this size of flooring, so for the first several days it may be necessary to place a piece of hardware cloth with ¼-inch openings over the original flooring. Also, goslings are taller than chicks and in some models can burn their heads or eyes on the heating element. While new units are expensive, this type of brooder requires limited floorspace, is easily cleaned, protects young birds from predators and provides sanitary conditions.

Draft Guards — For the first two weeks of the brooding period, it is recommended that draft guards be used with hover brooders or heat lamps to shield goslings from harmful drafts and to keep them from wandering too far away from the heat source and piling up in corners. Homemade guards can be made with twelve-inch boards, welded wire covered with feed sacks or straw or hay bales. Commercially prepared corrugated cardboard guards are also available and can be used several times. Draft guards should form a circle two or three feet from the outside edge of the canopy, or three or four feet from heat lamps, the first several days, gradually being moved outward until no longer needed.

Brooding Temperature

The temperature at which goslings should be brooded depends on such factors as the birds' age, outside temperature, humidity of the air and dryness of the litter. As a general rule, the temperature at floor level under brooders should be approximately 85° to 90° F (30° to 32° C) the first seven days, and then lowered 5° F (2.5° C) each successive week. Goslings can survive temperatures of 50° F (10° C) or lower when they are six to eight weeks old and fairly well feathered, but still need to be protected from drastic temperature changes. Chilled birds grow poorly and are subject to pneumonia and death.

The behavior of goslings is the best guide to the correct temperature. If the birds are noisy and huddle together under the heat source, they are cold and additional heat should be supplied. When they stay away from the heat or pant,

A portable brooder house with wire-covered run

they are too warm and the temperature needs to be lowered. The proper amount of heat is being provided when goslings sleep peacefully under the brooder or move about contentedly, eating and drinking.

It is extremely important that goslings of all ages be able to get away from the heat source whenever they choose. Overheating can result in slow growth, retarded feathering, cannibalism or an intestinal disorder which is characterized by a pasty vent.

FLOORSPACE

Because of their large size and heavy drinking habits, goslings need three to five times the floorspace normally allowed for chickens. When brooded on bedding, a minimum of ¾ square foot of floorspace per bird should be allowed the first week, 1½ the second week, and 4 to 5 square feet up to four weeks. These figures can be reduced by approximately one-third when wire floors are used. As soon as goslings are comfortable outside — one to two weeks of age in mild weather — it is beneficial to give them access to a grassy yard, allowing ten to twenty square feet of space per bird. This additional space helps keep the inside bedding drier and reduces sanitation problems.

LITTER

When goslings are reared on bedding, a thick layer of absorbent and mold-free litter is needed to keep the brooding area from becoming a sloppy, smelly mess. A wide variety of materials make satisfactory bedding: wood shavings, peanut and coffee hulls, peat moss, crushed corn cobs and chopped straw or flax — to name a few. Fine-textured bedding such as sawdust can be used, but it should be covered with burlap for the first several days to prevent goslings from eating it. Don't use newspapers since newly hatched goslings have difficulty walking on such smooth surfaces and can be permanently crippled with spraddled legs.

Starting with at least three to four inches of bedding, add new litter as needed. Soggy and caked bedding should be removed and replaced with dry material. The daily stirring of litter and placing of all waterers over pits on wire-covered platforms greatly reduces wet bedding problems. In warm weather, flies which carry filth and disease will become a problem if the quality of the litter is allowed to deteriorate.

WIRE FLOORS

An effective way of eliminating wet litter is to brood goslings on raised wire floors. Care must be taken to keep chilling drafts from circulating up through the floor. To prevent manure buildup, wire mesh used as flooring should have openings at least 1" x ½". Until the birds are a week old, a finer mesh wire pad can be used to keep the goslings' feet from slipping through the holes.

YARDS AND PASTURES

As soon as they are comfortable outside, goslings can be turned out in a grassy yard or pasture, giving them much needed exercise, fresh air and sunlight. The grass they consume not only reduces their need for costly feed, but also enriches their diet with protein, minerals, vitamins and fiber. Goslings cannot utilize grasses that are coarse, dry or wiry. Keeping grass mowed, watered and fertilized encourages succulent vegetation.

In the downy stage, goslings easily become soaked and chilled. When allowed outside, they should be put under cover each time it rains hard until they are five to six weeks old. Once they have a good thatch of feathers on their shoulders and back, a shelter where they can find refuge from precipitation is adequate protection during the day.

SWIMMING WATER

Goslings enjoy swimming as soon as they can walk, but bathing water is not required, or necessarily desirable, especially the first month. Artificially hatched and brooded goslings easily become soaked and can chill or drown if allowed to swim before their underbodies are feathered. Even when goslings are brooded by their natural parents, it is safest to keep them out of water until they are at least two weeks old.

To protect goslings from becoming soaked or drowning, all water containers which they can enter should have gradually sloping sides with good footing to permit easy exit for wet swimmers. If you do supply swimming water in receptacles having steep or slick sides, an exit ramp must be provided if drowning losses are to be avoided. Drowning and becoming drenched and chilled are the leading causes of gosling mortality in home goose flocks.

Geese of all ages that have been raised in confinement have been known to drown when turned out onto deep swimming water. Before allowing access

While okay for large, well-feathered goslings, water containers with steep slick sides, such as this tub, can be the demise of downy young.

to swimming water, birds can be conditioned by spraying them with water two or three times daily for several days. The spraying stimulates preening, which in turn oils the feathers and waterproofs them.

REVIVING WATERLOGGED GOSLINGS

Goslings sometimes get soaked through to the skin when they fall into a water container they can't get out of, play in their drinking water or get stranded in a rainstorm. In this condition, they chill, quickly lose mobility and will die if not promptly warmed. However, even when their bodies feel icy cold and they can scarcely move, goslings can often be revived — almost miraculously — if immediate action is taken.

First, rub down the waterlogged victim with a soft, absorbent cloth. Being careful not to overheat the curried survivor, place it in a warm (85° to 90° F or 30° to 32° C) location, such as under a heat lamp or in a brooder. After the gosling is active, provide feed and lukewarm drinking water.

DRINKING WATER

Goslings can thrive only if they have a constant supply of reasonably clean drinking water. As one hatcheryman so aptly stated, "These birds are born thirsty and stay that way." Drinking troughs or fountains should be designed so that young birds cannot get excessively wet. However, to lessen the possibility of choking and eye infections, it is helpful if the water is sufficiently deep and wide to allow the birds to submerge their heads.

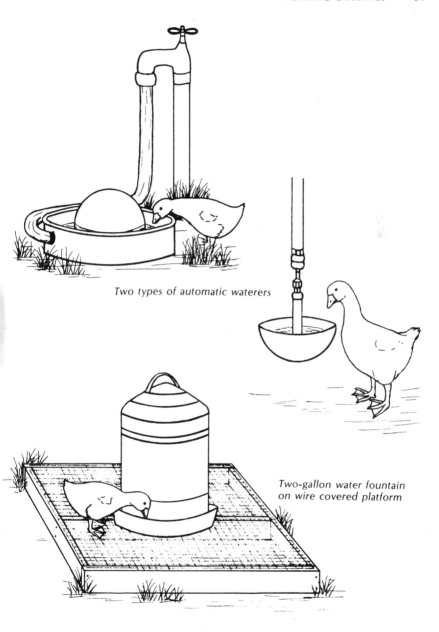

Two types of automatic waterers

Two-gallon water fountain
on wire covered platform

Adequate receptacles should be provided so their contents are not quickly exhausted and the goslings left without water. Placing water containers on screen-covered platforms is helpful in keeping the watering area dry and sanitary. Waterers should be rinsed out daily and occasionally disinfected.

Fast growing goslings need a steady supply of drinking water.

FEEDING PROGRAMS

Thanks to the fine foraging ability of goslings, and to the wide availability of commercially prepared rations, the feeding of goslings does not need to be a laborious or time-consuming task. Nevertheless, you should acquaint yourself with the nutritional requirements of goslings to insure against the possibility of malnutrition which can result in retarded growth, weak legs, unnecessary health problems and high mortality.

As with all poultry, the rate at which goslings grow is controlled by the quantity and quality of the feed they consume. For maximum growth they need a diet that provides 20 to 22 percent crude protein from zero to three weeks of age, and 15 to 16 percent after three weeks. However, when goslings are being raised for breeders or if you are not planning to butcher them before they are fourteen to sixteen weeks old, they will grow satisfactorily and remain healthy when started and grown on a 16 percent protein ration that is fortified with adequate vitamins and minerals.

For the first week or two, small pelleted (3/32″) or coarse crumbled feed is preferred; thereafter, larger pellets (3/16″) will give the best results. Fine powdery mash can choke goslings when fed dry, and up to a quarter of the feed is wasted. If used, finely ground feed is better utilized when slightly moistened with water or milk to a consistency that will form a loose crumbly ball when compressed in the hand. To avoid spoilage and the possibility of food poisoning, a new batch should be mixed up at each feeding.

TABLE 9   SUGGESTED FEEDING SCHEDULE FOR GOSLINGS

Type of Gosling	0 to 3 Weeks Amount of 20-22% CP Starter Feed per Bird Daily	4 to 12 Weeks Amount of 16-18% CP Grower Feed per Bird Daily	13 to 26 Weeks Pounds of 16% CP Developer Feed per Bird Daily
Broiler	Free choice	Free choice	
Lightweight Breed	Free choice	Free choice for 3 to 5 minutes once daily*	.20-.40**
Mediumweight Breed	Free choice	Same as above*	.25-.45**
Heavyweight Breed	Free choice	Same as above*	.30-.50**

These are general recommendations only and the actual quantity of feed required by goslings is highly dependent on the availability of forage, climatic conditions and the quality of feed (e.g., birds require larger amounts of high fiber feed than low fiber foods to meet their energy requirements).

*If goslings do not have access to tender forage, feeding should be increased to twice daily.

**The lower figure is for birds on pasture, the higher for confinement reared birds or when forage has dried up or is not available.

Key: CP = Crude Protein

The measure of feed that should be allowed for each bird is dependent on a number of factors, including breed, age of the goslings, availability of tender forage and the rate of growth you wish the birds to attain. Also to be considered is that geese which are fed well the first four to six months of their life mature quicker and are more likely to reproduce successfully as yearlings than goslings that are raised on restricted amounts of concentrated feeds.

To induce rapid growth, goslings should be supplied a concentrated ration free choice the first two or three weeks. After this time, they can be limited to two feedings daily, when they should be given all the feed they can clean up in ten to fifteen minutes. Once an abundant supply of succulent grass is available, goslings two weeks and older can be limited to one feeding a day of concentrated feed. Giving the birds their meal in the evening will encourage them to graze during the day. Whenever the amount of grain or mixed feed is being restricted, goslings must have tender grasses and clovers. Young geese can starve on some types of weeds and tough, dry or mature grass.

Natural — When grown on fertile soil, fast-growing, tender young grass (before it joints) and clover are relatively high in protein and provide an adequate diet even for newly hatched goslings if top growth rate is not important. However, at the risk of being repetitious, I'll state once again that geese of all ages, and especially young goslings, cannot be expected to live on dry, tough or mature forage. (See page 104 under the heading of Pasture for instructions on how to keep grasses succulent.) Wild geese and their broods can roam from one area to another in search of greener pastures, while domestic birds are usually limited to what's available within confining fences. Even when lush pasture is available, it is usually advisable to supply goslings with concentrated feed for at least two or three weeks to get them off to a fast start. Thereafter, one to two pounds of pellets or grain per bird per week normally is adequate as long as good pasture is on hand.

These ten-day-old White Chinese goslings are exploring their expanding world.

Grains — Once goslings are seven to ten days old they can be fed cracked, rolled or small whole grains, if coarse sand or chick-sized granite grit is also provided. However, since grains by themselves are not a balanced diet, goslings must also have access to succulent pasture or a prepared protein, vitamin and mineral supplement if they are expected to grow well and remain healthy.

Home-Mixed — If the necessary ingredients can be obtained locally at a reasonable price, you may want to mix your own feed. In Tables 10 and 11 you'll find samples of simple formulas that can be mixed at home for a flock of goslings. These rations are not as sophisticated as commercial feeds, but will give good results in most situations if correctly mixed. The formulas in Table 12 can also be home-blended if a vitamin:mineral premix — often available from feed mills — is used. (See Appendix A for instructions on formulating rations that use local foodstuffs.)

You do not need fancy equipment to mix goose feed. A large tub can be used for small quantities. Simply put ingredients in the tub and mix with your hands or a stick. Another method is to pile measured components in layers on a clean floor and mix with a scoop shovel. If you're going to mix a substantial quantity of feed, you may want to use a cement mixer or a barrel mounted on a stand and outfitted with a handle, door and ball bearings. More important than the method used for mixing is that the ingredients be thoroughly combined. To prevent vitamins from deteriorating and fats and oils from turning rancid, no more than a four-week supply of feed — three weeks or less if ground grains are used — should be prepared at a time during warm (70° F or 21° C or above) weather.

TABLE 10   HOME-MIXED STARTING RATION (0 to 3 weeks)

Ingredient	No. 1 Small Quantity		No. 2 Large Quantity	
Ground or cracked corn, wheat or milo	12	cups	62	lbs.
Soybean meal solv. (50% protein)	3½	cups	16	lbs.
Meat and bone meal (50% protein)	⅔	cup	4	lbs.
Brewer's dried yeast	2	cups	7½	lbs.
Crushed calf manna or	1	cup	5	lbs.
½ dried whey, ½ wheat bran				
Alfalfa meal (17% protein)	½	cup	2	lbs.
Molasses, livestock grade	⅓	cup	3	lbs.
Dicalcium phosphate (18.5% P)	1	tbsp.	¼	lb.
Iodized salt	1	tsp.	¼	lb.
Totals	20	cups	100	lbs.
Chopped succulent greens	Free choice		Free choice	
Sand or chick-size granite grit	Free choice		Free choice	
Chick-size oyster shells or crushed dried egg shells	Free choice		Free choice	

Cod liver oil: If birds do not receive direct sunlight, which enables them to synthesize vitamin D, sufficient cod liver oil must be added to the ration to provide 500 International Chick Units (ICU) of vitamin D3 per pound of feed.

TABLE 11   HOME-MIXED GROWING RATIONS (4 to 12 weeks)

Ingredient	No. 3 Corn Base pounds	No. 4 Wheat Base pounds	No. 5 Milo Base pounds
Cracked yellow corn	75.00	—	—
Whole soft wheat	—	78.00	—
Milo (grain sorghum)	—	—	75.00
Soybean meal solv. (50% protein)	8.00	5.00	8.00
Brewer's dried yeast	6.00	6.00	6.00
Meat and bone meal (50% protein)	4.00	4.00	4.00
Alfalfa meal (17% protein)	3.00	3.00	3.00
Dried whey or calf manna	3.00	3.00	3.00
Limestone flour or oyster shells	.50	.50	.50
Dicalcium phosphate (18.5% P)	.25	.25	.25
Iodized salt	.25	.25	.25
Totals (lbs.)	100.00	100.00	100.00
Sand or chick-size granite grit	Free choice	Free choice	Free choice
Succulent greens (eliminate when pasture is available)	Free choice	Free choice	Free choice

Cod liver oil: See Table 10.

Commercial — In areas where large numbers of ducks and geese are raised commercially, premixed starter and grower feeds are sometimes available. If these feeds are used, the instructions on the label should be followed. If you can't find rations specifically formulated for goslings, then a non-medicated chick starter or a general purpose poultry feed can be used. As long as they aren't medicated, chicken feeds usually give satisfactory results if they're supplemented with additional niacin. Laying rations should not be fed to growing goslings since these feeds have an excess of calcium, which can cause serious problems.

People frequently ask what to feed their goslings when they can't find a non-medicated chick or waterfowl starter ration at their local feed stores. When we raise a small flock of goslings and do not have starter and grower feeds custom mixed, we purchase a 16 percent protein, non-medicated, general purpose poultry crumbles (with not more than 1 percent calcium), and for extra protein, vitamins and minerals, mix in a small portion of livestock grade brewer's dried yeast plus medicated turkey or broiler starter that is 24 to 26 percent protein. We've had satisfactory results by combining these feeds and supplement in the following proportions: for goslings up to two weeks of age — ten pounds of the 16 percent protein general purpose crumbles, five pounds of the 24 to 26 percent protein medicated turkey or broiler starter and two cups of dried brewer's yeast; and for goslings two to eight weeks of age — thirteen pounds of the 16 percent feed, two pounds of the turkey or broiler starter and two cups of brewer's yeast.

If a large enough number of goslings are being raised, you may want to have a local feed mill custom mix your feed. The formulas given in Table 12 are for complete rations that will provide a balanced diet if mixed properly and not stored for more than four weeks (less in hot weather). Ration numbers 6, 7 and 8 are to be fed to goslings up to three weeks of age, and numbers 9, 10 and 11 from three to approximately sixteen weeks.

Proper Storage of Feed

Careful planning should be given to where feed is going to be kept. If not stored properly, feeds — especially mixed rations containing ground or cracked grains — are highly perishable. Direct sunlight destroys some vitamins, warm temperatures cause fats to turn rancid and dampness encourages harmful bacteria and mold growth. Rats, mice, ground squirrels and other rodents are also rough on feeds. A single rat can consume or spoil fifty pounds or more of feed over the course of a year. Insects are also a problem in some localities.

Feeds should be stored in metal containers such as garbage cans or empty barrels that have been de-toxified if they originally contained a potentially harmful product. As a general rule of thumb, mixed rations should not be stored for longer than four weeks.

Niacin Requirements

Since young waterfowl require two or three times more niacin than chicks (see Niacin Deficiency, page 136), goslings raised in confinement on niacin deficient rations — such as commercial chick feeds — must have niacin added to their feed or water. A niacin deficiency can result in severely crippled legs, stunted growth and poor feathering. Niacin is a common ingredient in vitamin mixes and can also be bought at drug stores in tablet form. Adding 5 to 7½ pounds of livestock grade dried brewer's yeast per 100 pounds of chicken feed (or for small quantities two to three cups of yeast per ten pounds of feed) will prevent a niacin deficiency.

TABLE 12   COMPLETE RATIONS FOR GOSLINGS (Pelleted)

Ingredient	No. 6 Corn Base Starter lbs/ton	No. 7 Wheat Base Starter lbs/ton	No. 8 Milo Base Starter lbs/ton	No. 9 Corn Base Grower lbs/ton	No. 10 Wheat Base Grower lbs/ton	No. 11 Milo Base Grower lbs/ton
Ground yellow corn	1134	—	—	1357	—	—
Ground soft wheat	—	1337	—	—	1538	—
Ground milo (grain sorghum)	—	—	1121	—	—	1337
Soybean meal solv. (50% protein)	472	440	474	320	289	320
Ground barley	200	—	200	200	—	200
Meat and bone meal (50% protein)	80	80	80	40	40	40
Alfalfa meal, dehy. (17% protein)	40	40	40	20	20	20
DL-Methionine (98%)	2	2	3	1	2	2
Stabilized animal fat	25	40	30	—	40	20
Soybean/corn oil	—	14	5	—	10	—
Dicalcium phosphate (18.5% P)	11	11	11	18	17	17
Limestone flour (38% Ca)	8	8	8	16	16	16
Iodized salt	8	8	8	8	8	8
Vitamin:mineral premix	20	20	20	20	20	20
Totals (lbs.)	2000	2000	2000	2000	2000	2000
Vitamin:Mineral Premix						
Vit. A (millions of IU/ton)	9.0	9.0	9.0	6.5	6.5	6.5
Vit. D3 (millions of ICU/ton)	1.2	1.2	1.2	1.0	1.0	1.0
Vit. E (thousands of IU/ton)	12.0	12.0	12.0	10.0	10.0	10.0
Vit. K (gm/ton)	2.0	2.0	2.0	1.5	1.5	1.5
Riboflavin (gm/ton)	6.0	6.0	6.0	4.0	4.0	4.0
Vit. B12 (mg/ton)	8.0	8.0	8.0	6.0	6.0	6.0
Niacin (gm/ton)	50.0	50.0	50.0	40.0	40.0	40.0
d-Calcium pantothenate (gm/ton)	8.0	4.0	4.0	8.0	4.0	4.0
Choline chloride (gm/ton)	300.0	—	300.0	200.0	—	200.0
Folic acid (gm/ton)	.5	.5	.5	.5	.5	.5
Manganese oxide (56% Mn, gm/ton)	110.0	110.0	110.0	110.0	110.0	110.0
Zinc oxide (80% Zn, gm/ton)	70.0	70.0	70.0	70.0	70.0	70.0
Copper sulfate (25% Cu, gm/ton)	18.0	18.0	18.0	18.0	18.0	18.0
Ground grain to make 20 lbs.	+	+	+	+	+	+
Totals (lbs.)	20.0	20.0	20.0	20.0	20.0	20.0
Calculated analysis						
Crude protein (%)	20.5	20.4	20.6	16.4	16.4	16.4
Lysine (%)	1.05	1.03	1.04	.77	.76	.76
Methionine + cystine (%)	.75	.74	.75	.60	.63	.59
Metabolizable energy (kcal/lb)	1359	1336	1353	1383	1361	1381
Calorie:protein ratio	66	66	66	84	83	84
Crude fiber (%)	3.0	2.8	3.4	2.8	2.6	3.1
Calcium (%)	.78	.80	.79	.77	.78	.77
Available phosphorus (%)	.41	.42	.41	.37	.36	.36
Vit. A (IU/lb, amount added)	4500	4500	4500	3250	3250	3250
Vit. D3 (ICU/lb, amount added)	600	600	600	500	500	500
Total niacin (mg/lb)	37	45	41	32	42	37

Grit and Calcium

Coarse sand or chick-sized granite grit should be kept before goslings free choice at all times, except when they're raised in confinement and fed nothing but finely ground feeds. Grit aids the gizzard in grinding, helping the birds get the most out of their feed and forage. When goslings are not receiving a complete ration containing sufficient calcium, limestone flour or chick-sized oyster shells should also be fed free choice.

Feeders

Goslings do not require elaborate dinnerware. For the first day or two, feed should be placed in containers where the goslings cannot help but find it. Jar lids, shallow cans and egg flats are excellent for this purpose. Once the goslings have located their feed and are eating well, they should be fed in trough feeders to reduce wastage. Feeders can be purchased or constructed at home out of scrap materials. Homemade troughs should be designed so they do not tip over as goslings jostle for eating space. To keep poorly mannered birds out of the feeder, a spinner can be attached across the top.

To guarantee that all goslings receive their fair share, be sure to provide ample feeding space so all birds can eat at once, especially when they are limited to one or two feedings daily. By filling troughs no more than half full, the amount of feed that is wasted can be significantly reduced.

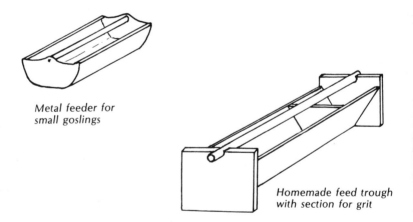

Metal feeder for
small goslings

Homemade feed trough
with section for grit

Creep Feeding

When goslings are brooded by their natural parents, it is sometimes desirable to feed the young birds separately from the adult geese. This goal can be accomplished by devising a creep feeder, where goslings can eat without competing with the grown birds. The basic component of the creep feeder is a panel or doorway having openings small enough so only goslings can pass

Creep feeder

through and gain access to the feed trough. This panel can be placed across a corner of the goose yard or in the entrance way of a shed.

Dimensions for the portals will vary according to the breed raised, and you'll probably need to do some experimenting to find what size works best for your geese. However, as a general rule, passageways five inches wide and eight inches high will keep the adult birds out while allowing goslings up to five to six weeks of age to enter.

MANAGING GOSLING BROILERS

Broilers or junior geese are managed to produce the quickest possible growth and tenderest meat. The breeds best suited for this practice are Embden, White Chinese, Pilgrim, American Buff or Embden-White Chinese crosses. With good management, Embden broilers are capable of weighing ten to twelve pounds at eight to twelve weeks of age on approximately thirty-five to forty-five pounds of concentrated feed. When good pasture is available, feed consumption can be reduced to about twenty to thirty pounds per bird.

To stimulate fast growth, gosling broilers must have limited exercise, plenty of cool shade, a continuous supply of concentrated feed and twenty-four hours of light daily. They are ready to butcher as soon as they are in full feather and carry the desired amount of finish. If held beyond nine to twelve weeks, feed

TABLE 13   TYPICAL GROWTH RATE AND FEED EFFICIENCY OF LARGE TYPE
EMBDEN GOSLINGS RAISED IN SMALL FLOCKS

Treatment	Age weeks	Average Live Weight pounds	Feed Consumed per Gosling pounds	Feed Consumed per Lb. of Bird pounds
Fed free choice 20% protein,	6	8.0	14.0	1.8
1350 kcal/lb ration from 0 to	8	10.2	21.5	2.1
4 weeks; then 16% protein,	10	11.3	28.0	2.5
1350 kcal/lb ration free	12	12.2	35.0	2.9
choice up to 24 weeks. Kept	16	12.7	45.5	3.6
in confinement from 0 to 2	20	13.8	57.0	4.1
weeks, then given access to	24	14.4	68.0	4.7
good pasture. Exposed to 24				
hours of light daily from 0				
to 8 weeks; thereafter				
natural light only.				

conversion decreases rapidly (see Table 13) and they'll commence to molt, making it difficult to pick them, due to pin feathers, until they are sixteen to twenty-six weeks of age.

PRODUCING LEAN GOSLINGS FOR MEAT

While some people relish juicy, well-fattened goose meat, medical research indicates that most of us North Americans would be better off if we reduced our consumption of animal fats. There are a number of practices that can be employed to produce goose meat that is considerably less greasy than the roasting birds normally found in the grocery store.

First of all, one can raise a breed that naturally has less body fat, such as the Chinese or African. Secondly, rather than pushing goslings for the fastest possible growth, they should be allowed to forage a substantial portion of their diet. In addition to their gleanings, the birds should be given just enough grain or pellets to keep them in good flesh and growing well. When butchered at twenty-two to twenty-six weeks, the fat content of geese raised in this manner is similar to wild geese.

MARKING GOSLINGS

There are situations when it is desirable to mark individual goslings so that they can be positively identified at a later date. A variety of methods are available, including the use of leg or wing bands, and the notching, perforating or tattooing of the webbing between the bird's toes. Numbered neck collars are available for larger geese. (Bands, neck collars, toe punches and tattoo pliers can be purchased from feed stores and poultry equipment suppliers — see Appendix I.)

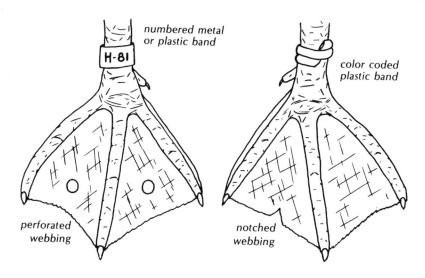

numbered metal
or plastic band

H-81

color coded
plastic band

perforated
webbing

notched
webbing

Marking birds for positive identification

When leg bands are applied, be sure to use rings that are sufficiently large to permit blood circulation, but yet tight enough to stay on. If toe punching is used, the perforations should be at least a quarter inch in diameter to prevent them from growing closed in a short period of time.

Managing Adult Geese

Mature geese are hardy and independent creatures. When kept in small flocks and allowed to roam in a barnyard or field, they require less attention than all other domestic birds, with the possible exception of guinea fowl.

BASIC GUIDELINES

Methods of caring for adult geese vary according to climates, breeds and people's experiences and goals. However, in the breeding of geese, there are eight basic guidelines which must be followed if you desire consistently good results.

Protect your birds from predators — Although few mature geese die from disease or exposure to severe weather, quite a number are lost to predators such as dogs, foxes, coyotes and large owls. In areas where there are predators, geese should be penned — every night — in a securely fenced yard or a well-ventilated building.

Supply a balanced diet and avoid medicated feeds — A common cause of reproductive failure in geese is inadequate nutrition. Also, some medications commonly used in chicken and turkey rations apparently reduce hatchability in goose eggs.

Provide a steady supply of drinking water — Geese do not need swimming water to thrive, but they must have a constant supply of reasonably clean drinking water, preferably supplied in containers that are deep enough for the birds to submerge their heads.

Furnish suitable living conditions — Forcing geese to live in pens deeply covered with mud and manure or containing putrid waterholes is an invitation for disease and parasites.

Disturb them no more than necessary — All waterfowl, especially geese, thrive on tranquility. Egg production and fertility can be drastically curtailed if geese are frequently agitated.

Do not catch or carry them by their legs — The legs of geese are not as strong as those of chickens, and these big birds can be crippled if caught and held by them.

Make sure you have both males and females — Novices often have a tough time distinguishing gender, and it's not unusual for non-producing "pairs" to consist of two ganders or two geese.

Don't harass or tease your charges — When mistreated, geese — especially when kept in small flocks — can develop the obnoxious and painful habits of biting and wing beating anyone who trespasses onto their territory.

HOUSING

When fed sufficient quantities of high energy feed during winter months, geese are amazingly resistant to cold and wet weather and require less housing than other domestic birds. In fact, geese usually prefer to remain outside in all but the most severe weather.

In mild climates, geese can be raised without artificial shelter as long as shade is available during warm weather. If furnished with a thick layer of dry bedding, a semicircular windbreak four to five feet high made of straw bales, and facing away from frigid prevailing winds, will provide sufficient protection in regions where temperatures rarely dip to 0° F (-18° C). A more substantial shelter is usually required in areas where extremely low temperatures are common. However, even when the thermometer plunges below 0° F (-18° C), some goosekeepers living in northern climates leave their birds outside, day and night all winter long, if there is open water on which the geese can swim.

One of the main reasons for housing geese at all is to protect them from predators since they perch either on the ground or on water. A tightly fenced yard with wire at least four feet high is sufficient to stop most losses to predation. However, in localities where bandits such as bobcats, raccoons and Great Horned Owls are in residence, it is best to lock geese in a varmint-proof building or wire-covered enclosure at night.

Suitable shelter for a few geese

If you decide that a goosehouse would be advantageous, but don't have an empty building available, a simple shed-like structure, such as shown in the accompanying illustration, can be constructed. This practical shelter is portable, and besides providing winter shelter for adult geese, can be utilized as a nesting area or feeding station and for brooding goslings or other young birds.

Geese are more inclined to enter buildings if the roof is not too low, so walls at least four feet high are recommended. Three solid walls and an open or wire-covered front are suggested except in regions with harsh winters, where a partially closed front is advantageous. Geese fare poorly if forced to stay in stuffy, damp quarters, so good ventilation is essential even in cold weather. A wire netting floor can be installed to keep rodents and digging predators from excavating under walls and gaining entrance. Placing the shed on a slope or building up the floor six to twelve inches above ground level insures good drainage. If the goosehouse is located in a low spot, water will accumulate, making it impossible to keep the litter from becoming a mucky mess.

If your geese are housed overnight, allow at least 7½ to 10 square feet of floorspace per bird. If you anticipate keeping your geese inside continuously for a period of time, a minimum of fifteen to twenty square feet of floorspace is usually required to keep the pen reasonably clean and to prevent the birds from fighting excessively.

The Goose Yard

Most successful goosekeepers have a fenced yard where birds are shut in at night — continuously if space is limited — for protection from dogs, foxes and coyotes. The yard should have good drainage, be free of stagnant waterholes or deep mud, and provide a minimum of twenty-five to fifty square feet of ground space per bird — 100 or more square feet per goose if they are not turned out during the day.

Where soil has poor drainage, build up the center of the yard higher than the edges and cover it with sand, straw or wood shavings. When selecting the site for your goose yard, keep in mind that geese will strip the bark off young trees and the manure from a dense population of birds can also kill young trees.

Bedding

Geese can survive cold, wet weather only if their feathers are kept reasonably clean and in good condition. Forcing waterfowl to live in filthy yards or buildings results in badly worn feathers that lose much of their water shedding capabilities. The floors of buildings where geese are kept should be covered with at least four or five inches of absorbent litter such as wood shavings or straw. In muddy or snow-covered yards, mounds of bedding six to twelve inches thick should be provided where all birds can roost comfortably. Add new bedding as required.

Shade

Geese are cool weather birds and they suffer if forced to remain in the hot sun. When natural shade is lacking, a shelter should be provided which will supply adequate shade for all the birds. Feeders can be located under this cover for protection from the weather.

This type of shelter provides geese with shade and protects their food from the elements.

Nests

Geese do not require fancy accommodations for their eggs, but having adequate nests will help produce cleaner eggs and reduces the chances of eggs being broken or exposed to the elements. So geese have time to become familiar with them, nests should be installed several weeks before the first eggs are expected. If eggs are going to be gathered daily for eating or setting in an incubator or under a foster hen, one nest for every six to eight geese is sufficient. When eggs are left for natural incubation, each female must have her own nesting site if satisfactory results are expected. Two or more geese laying and setting in the same nest usually results in a bundle of eggs, but few — if any — goslings.

For most breeds, nests about two feet square are recommended. Goose nests are placed on the ground so they do not require solid bottoms. However, covering the nest floors with burlap or boards aids in keeping the eggs clean. For shade, outside nests should either be located under a tree or bush or have a top and sides. To shield eggs from the warm midday and afternoon sun, nests should face north or northeast in the Northern Hemisphere. Keeping nests well furnished with clean nesting material such as straw or dried grass encourages birds to use them and results in fewer broken or badly soiled eggs.

Covered nests protect eggs and geese from precipitation and the hot sun.

When visiting goose breeders, one can see many types of nests in use, including heaps of straw on the ground under a tree, beside a bush or between bales of hay; used tires filled with dry grass; wooden nests with A-frame or sloping roofs; discarded barrels with tops removed and lying on their sides; and evacuated doghouses.

When tire nests are used, their side walls should be packed with straw so that eggs don't get pushed into the tire or goslings get trapped as the goose vacates the nest with her brood. Several precautions also need to be taken when geese are allowed to set in barrels. First, the barrel needs to be stacked, blocked or entrenched so it will not roll away in a brisk wind or if a large animal pushes against it. Secondly, once the weather warms up, incubating geese can be driven out of barrel nests by the heat if a dozen one inch holes aren't punched near the top in the back for ventilation. Thirdly, to keep eggs off the steel floor and to provide moisture, a board six to eight inches wide should be fastened across the front, five or six inches of damp sand or dirt put in the bottom and then a good armful of straw or grass added for nesting material.

DRINKING WATER

In mild and hot weather, geese must have a constant supply of reasonably clean drinking water during the daylight hours. So the birds can wash out their nostrils and rinse their eyes, waterers should be designed to provide water that is a minimum of five to six inches deep. Buckets, dishpans and hot water tanks (cut in half vertically) make satisfactory drinking containers. The above mentioned containers can be automatically filled by placing them under a slowly dripping faucet or rigging them up with an automatic float. Floats often need to be covered to keep geese from chewing on them.

A bucket placed under a slowly dripping faucet or outfitted with a float valve supplies adequate drinking water for 50 to 100 adult geese.

Placing water receptacles on wire covered platforms greatly aids in keeping the drinking area sanitary.

Geese should be given fresh water at least several times a week. Because they frequently wash their bills and faces, drinking water rapidly becomes clouded, making it nearly impossible to keep clean water before them. While it is not necessary to keep their water clear at all times, it must never be allowed to become putrid.

Placing water fountains on platforms covered with welded wire or wooden slats keeps unsanitary mudholes from developing around the watering area. To prevent manure from building up on the platform, the wire netting should have openings one inch square. A pit twelve inches deep can be excavated underneath the platform and filled with gravel for additional protection.

If forced to, geese can survive for a short time by eating soft snow. However, it is preferable to give them lukewarm drinking water several times daily when all available liquid is frozen. In cool weather when they are locked up at night, geese can get by without drinking water as long as feed is not available.

SWIMMING WATER

Geese can be raised successfully without water for swimming if a supply of fresh drinking water is provided in containers that are sufficiently deep for the birds to submerge their entire heads. However, having suitable bathing facilities provides hours of entertainment as the geese frolic and bathe, and usually results in cleaner birds, fewer sore feet, better fertility and less trouble with external parasites.

If your property is not blessed with a natural pond or stream, bathing water can be provided in a small cement pond or containers such as a large tub, split barrel or a child's fiberglass or ridged plastic wading pool. Small dirt ponds usually are not recommended since they are difficult to keep clean and waterfowl can quickly turn them into unsanitary mudholes. Geese must not be allowed to swim in or drink filthy, stagnant water.

Small bodies of water that do not have a continuous source of fresh water must be drained and cleaned at regular intervals to keep them from becoming dangerously polluted. When planning cement ponds, it's important that they be designed for easy emptying and cleaning (see illustration on pond construction). Also keep in mind that it requires a good many gallons of water to fill even a modest-size pool (a pond ten feet square with a depth of twelve inches holds 748 gallons!), so keep the dimensions within the limitations of your water supply. A collar of cement, sand or gravel several feet wide around the perimeter of a pond is helpful in keeping geese from drilling with their bills and reduces the amount of mud they track in on their feet. Portable bathing containers such as wading pools should be moved frequently to prevent muddy conditions from developing.

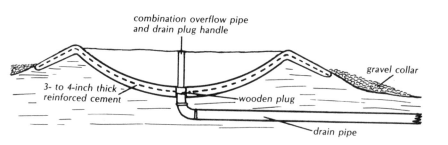

Homemade ponds should be constructed so they can be easily drained. If cleaned frequently, a pool with a diameter of 5 to 6 feet and a water depth of 12 inches is adequate for 25 to 50 adult geese.

NUTRITION

As with all livestock, the size, productivity and disease resistance of geese is controlled to a large degree by the quantity and quality of the food they eat. Because geese are active grazers, people sometimes assume that they'll never have to feed their birds anything but grass. However, in most areas, succulent forage is not available in sufficient quantity the year around and geese will need a supplement of grain and/or mixed feed. Even when tender young grass is on hand, a light feeding daily of concentrated feed (1 to 1½ pounds per bird per week) is recommended under most situations to guard against vitamin and mineral deficiencies.

If you desire top egg production and hatchability from your breeding flock, three to four weeks before the first eggs are expected and throughout the laying season, a breeding ration containing a minimum of 18 to 20 percent crude protein (20 to 22 percent protein for Canada, Egyptian and Dewlap Toulouse) should be fed free choice. Geese lay best when semifat, but obesity must be avoided since such a condition can permanently damage the birds' reproductive organs. When geese are laying, a sudden change in the kind or quantity of feed normally results in a drastic reduction or complete halt in egg production and can throw the females into a premature molt which often means no more eggs until the following year.

Between breeding seasons, adult geese can be fed a maintenance ration containing 12 to 13 percent crude protein, and fed just enough to keep them in good health. To keep warm during cold spells, geese must consume considerably more food than during warmer weather. Yellow corn and wheat are excellent heat producing foods and a snack of one or the other of these grains shortly before dark helps the birds maintain body warmth through long winter nights.

TABLE 14   SUGGESTED FEEDING SCHEDULE FOR ADULT GEESE

Type of Goose	Maintenance Period When Birds Are Not Producing		3 to 4 Weeks Prior to and Throughout the Laying Season	3 Weeks Prior to Butchering Mature Geese
	Lbs. of 12% CP Holding Feed per Bird Daily		Lbs. of 18-20% CP Breeder Feed per Bird Daily	Lbs. of High Energy Feed per Bird Daily
	a	b		
Lightweight	.15-.20	.35-.50	Free choice	Free choice
Mediumweight	.15-.25	.40-.55	Free choice	Free choice
Heavyweight	.20-.30	.45-.60	Free choice	Free choice

These are general recommendations only and the actual quantity of feed required by geese is highly dependent on the availability of forage, climatic conditions and the quality of feed (e.g., birds require larger amounts of high fiber feed than low fiber foods to meet their energy requirements).

a—For birds on good pasture.

b—For birds in confinement or when pasture is poor quality.

Key: CP = Crude Protein

Feeding Programs

There are a variety of methods available to the small flock owner for supplying the nutritional requirements of geese. For persons interested in raising their birds with the least bother, purchasing a prepared poultry feed is usually the best solution. On the other hand, for those who are more interested in economy and are willing to spend the time, nearly all the feed required by a modest-sized flock of geese can be grown at home.

Natural — The least costly scheme for feeding geese is to make them forage for their food. This alternative is practical only when top egg production is not important and where natural foods such as succulent grasses, clovers, fruits and edible grass seeds are in abundant supply. While there will be times when geese can rustle most — or even all — of their grub, in many localities there will also be times when most of their food will need to be supplied in the form of grain and/or mixed rations since the quantity of natural feed fluctuates widely during the seasons of the year. Whenever geese are on pasture and are supplied a limited quantity of feed, they must be carefully observed for signs of malnourishment such as thinness, dull, ruffled feathers and slow, lumbering gaits.

Grains — Whole, cracked or rolled grains by themselves do not make a complete ration. However, if geese have access to good pasture or they are given a protein, vitamin and mineral concentrate (see Appendix A), a supplement of grain will often satisfy dietary needs, especially when the birds are not producing.

Most common cereal grains are acceptable waterfowl feed, including wheat, corn, sorghum grains, rye, barley and oats. Geese are not overly fond of the last two if not accustomed to them. However, barley and oats are good feeds and birds will learn to eat them if forced to do so.

Corn has a high fat content making it excellent food for birds during cold weather and for fattening poultry — if you want fat meat. But, if too much corn is fed (more than 60 percent of total diet) during periods of high temperatures, egg production may suffer, birds can molt prematurely or health problems develop.

Home-Mixed — If you have an economical source of grain and raise enough birds to make it practical, you may want to mix your own feed. Because mixed rations can spoil and lose food value — vitamins are especially

TABLE 15   HOME-MIXED RATIONS FOR ADULT GEESE

Ingredient	No. 12 Corn or Milo Base Holding pounds	No. 13 Wheat Base Holding pounds	No. 14 Corn or Milo Base Breeder pounds	No. 15 Wheat Base Breeder pounds
Whole milo or yellow corn	81.00	—	52.00	20.00
Whole soft wheat	—	83.00	10.00	44.00
Soybean meal solv. (50% protein)	2.00	—	10.00	8.00
Meat and bone meal (50% protein)	2.00	2.00	6.00	6.00
Alfalfa meal (17% protein)	4.00	4.00	4.00	4.00
Brewer's dried yeast	5.25	5.25	7.75	7.75
Molasses, livestock grade	3.00	3.00	3.00	3.00
Dried whey or calf manna	—	—	2.00	2.00
Limestone flour or oyster shells	1.50	1.50	4.00	4.00
Dicalcium phosphate (18.5% P)	1.00	1.00	1.00	1.00
Iodized salt	.25	.25	.25	.25
Totals (lbs.)	100.00	100.00	100.00	100.00

vulnerable to decay — no more than a three- to four-week supply should be prepared at a time.

The formulas in Table 15 are examples of simple rations that give satisfactory results under most situations, particularly when birds have access to pasture. The rations in Table 16 can also be made at home if a commercially prepared vitamin:mineral premix is utilized. Feel free to substitute the suggested ingredients with locally available products of similar food value. (See Appendix A for instructions on how to formulate rations.)

Commercial — A pre-mixed feed is the easiest way to supply your geese with an adequate diet. These rations are formulated to provide a balance of the important food elements.

Feeds manufactured for geese are not available in many localities. However, non-medicated chicken or general purpose poultry feeds usually work satisfactorily. When chicken feeds are used during the breeding season, the fertility and hatchability of goose eggs and the liveability of goslings is often improved by the addition of 2½ to 5 pounds of livestock grade brewer's yeast per 100 pounds of feed (or one to two cups per ten pounds of feed). Much less feed is wasted if geese are fed pellets rather than a fine mash or even crumbles. To avoid spoilage, don't purchase more than a month's supply of feed — even less in hot or exceptionally damp weather.

It may be practical to have a local feed mill custom mix your feed if you're raising a large number of geese. In Table 16 are several complete feed formulas that will give satisfactory results in most circumstances. The formula you use will depend on the time of year and should be based on the cheapest grain available in your area.

Importance of UGFs in Breeding Rations

Poultry nutritionists and breeders have long recognized that if certain ingredients are included in rations, growth can be accelerated in young birds and reproduction improved in adult stock. Because it is not understood why the performance of poultry improves when these feedstuffs are incorporated in their diet, these ingredients are said to have unidentified growth factors, or UGFs for short.

For maximum hatchability in goose eggs, it is important that the adult birds are supplied with a source of UGFs during the breeding season. This fact is especially true during winter and early spring when succulent, green forage is not available, or if the breeding stock is confined to grassless yards and are not supplied freshly chopped forage. Fresh, green grasses and legumes are important UGF contributors.

Unidentified factors are present in a variety of feedstuffs, with some of the most important ones being fish solubles, fish meal, meat meal or scraps, liver meal, dried whey, dried skim milk, dried buttermilk, dried brewer's yeast, fermentation dried solubles and fresh forage juice. To be effective, these ingredients need to be included at only 1 to 2 percent of the ration, seemingly

TABLE 16   COMPLETE RATIONS FOR ADULT GEESE (Pelleted)

Ingredient	No. 16 Corn Base Holding lbs/ton	No. 17 Wheat Base Holding lbs/ton	No. 18 Milo Base Holding lbs/ton	No. 19 Corn Base Bdr-Lyr lbs/ton	No. 20 Wheat Base Bdr-Lyr lbs/ton	No. 21 Milo Base Bdr-Lyr lbs/ton
Ground yellow corn	1236	—	—	1167	—	—
Ground soft wheat	—	1775	—	—	1367	—
Ground milo (grain sorghum)	—	—	1682	—	—	1176
Soybean meal solv. (50% protein)	144	105	200	360	325	350
Ground barley	500	—	—	200	—	200
Meat and bone meal (50% protein)	—	—	—	100	100	100
Alfalfa meal, dehy. (17% protein)	40	40	40	40	40	40
DL-Methionine (98%)	—	—	—	1	1.5	2
Stabilized animal fat	—	—	—	—	20	—
Soybean/corn oil	—	—	—	—	15	—
Dicalcium phosphate (18.5%)	30	30	30	24	24	24
Limestone flour (38% Ca)	20	21	20	80	79.5	80
Iodized salt	10	9	8	8	8	8
Vitamin:mineral premix	20	20	20	20	20	20
Totals (lbs.)	2000	2000	2000	2000	2000.0	2000

Vitamin:Mineral Premix

Vit. A (millions of IU/ton)	6.0	6.0	6.0	8.0	9.0	9.0
Vit. D3 (millions of ICU/ton)	.8	.8	.8	1.5	1.5	1.5
Vit. E (thousands of IU/ton)	5.0	5.0	5.0	10.0	10.0	10.0
Vit. K (gm/ton)	1.0	1.0	1.0	1.5	1.5	1.5
Riboflavin (gm/ton)	3.0	3.0	3.0	5.0	5.0	5.0
Vit. B12 (mg/ton)	4.0	4.0	4.0	8.0	8.0	8.0
Niacin (gm/ton)	30.0	30.0	30.0	50.0	50.0	50.0
d-Calcium pantothenate (gm/ton)	2.0	2.0	2.0	9.0	6.0	6.0
Choline chloride (gm/ton)	100.0	—	100.0	300.0	—	300.0
Folic acid (gm/ton)	—	—	—	.5	.5	.5
Biotin (mg/ton)	—	—	—	.2	.2	.2
Manganese oxide (56% Mn, gm/ton)	110.0	110.0	110.0	110.0	110.0	108.0
Zinc oxide (80% Zn, gm/ton)	70.0	70.0	70.0	70.0	70.0	70.0
Copper sulfate (25% Cu, gm/ton)	18.0	18.0	18.0	18.0	18.0	18.0
Ground grain to make 20 lbs.	+	+	+	+	+	+
Totals (lbs.)	20.0	20.0	20.0	20.0	20.0	20.0

Calculated Analysis

Crude protein (%)	12.3	12.1	12.9	18.3	18.0	18.2
Lysine (%)	.49	.46	.52	.87	.87	.87
Methionine + cystine (%)	.43	.42	.39	.62	.63	.62
Metabolizable energy (kcal/lb)	1357	1330	1414	1290	1265	1276
Calorie:protein ratio	110	110	110	70	70	70
Crude fiber (%)	3.3	2.8	3.1	2.9	2.7	3.3
Calcium (%)	.76	.80	.78	2.4	2.4	2.4
Available phosphorus (%)	.37	.38	.38	.57	.58	.53
Vit. A (IU/lb, amount added)	3000	3000	3000	4000	4500	4500
Vit. D3 (ICU/lb, amount added)	400	400	400	750	750	750
Total niacin (mg/lb)	29	38	32	37	45	41

with no appreciable gain by the inclusion of larger quantities. There also appears to be little, if any, advantage in including more than one or two of the listed UGF containing ingredients.

Pasture

Geese are such excellent grazers that under most situations it is impractical for the small flock owner to raise them in barren yards or pens. When adequate forage is available, mature geese need little more than drinking water, grit and a calcium supplement, except during the breeding season when a breeding ration is required for high egg production and reliable hatchability. It must be stressed that even adult geese cannot survive on dry, coarse or mature pasture nor on most species of non-grass weeds. When tender grass and/or clover is in limited supply or totally lacking, geese must be provided the equivalent of .3 to .6 pounds of concentrated feed per bird daily.

Without seeding a special plot, the majority of homesteads already have sufficient grass for a small flock of geese. These birds are compatible with other livestock and can share pasture with cows, horses, sheep and goats. Geese are sometimes kept in fenced yards around homes and used as lawnmowers. Warning: while goose manure — especially from birds whose diets consist largely of grass — is not nearly as pungent as that of chickens, geese often find sidewalks and patios perfect resting spots, and will leave behind prominent reminders of their presence. One way to avoid messy walks is to catch the grass as you mow it and then feed it to the geese.

In many situations, an orchard is a good location for a goose pasture. The grass helps smother out bothersome weeds and provides a protective, attractive ground cover. In addition, the shade from the trees promotes succulent growth during hot weather and the birds clean up diseased and insect infested windfall fruits.

These Embdens are enjoying a small creek at one of the poultry research farms at Oregon State University, Corvallis, Oregon.

Most grasses and clovers that produce tender forage and grow well in your region will make good permanent pasture for geese. In many localities, a combination of Orchard grass, Brome, Timothy, Perennial Rye and one or two clovers such as New Zealand White, Lodino, White Dutch or Red will yield good grazing throughout the spring, summer and early fall months. On low-lying land that is poorly drained, Reed Canary and Meadow Fescue can be added to the above mixture. Geese are not particularly fond of alfalfa, but they will learn to eat it if other grasses and clovers are not available. When grazed heavily, both clover and alfalfa must be rested periodically and allowed to grow back to avoid being killed. For advice on what varieties of grasses and legumes are especially well adapted for your soil and climate, check with your agriculture extension agent.

To remain palatable and productive during the warm months of summer and fall, pasture must be kept short, watered and fertilized. (We scatter the manure and bedding from the goose yard back on the pasture.) To increase productivity, we have found it helpful to divide our pasture into a number of smaller sections with three-foot high chicken netting and systematically rotate the geese from one pen to another. With this method, the birds clean up one section and then are moved to others until lush new growth has reappeared.

The amount of pasture needed per goose varies widely, depending on season, soil fertility, pasture management, types of grasses and your area's climate. Here in western Oregon, we have found that on well cared for turf, 60 to 100 adult geese can be run per acre of pasture during the spring and early summer months, but only about two-thirds as many from midsummer through the fall. If you find yourself short on grass, the productivity of your pasture can be significantly increased if birds are locked in a yard at night (this precaution reduces the amount of grass that is trampled and matted down with manure), and by using the already described rotation or strip pasture method.

Growing Goose Feed at Home

Besides providing grazing for geese, most — or all — of the feed needed for a flock of a dozen geese can be grown on half an acre of land. Field corn yields large ears that are easily harvested by hand and, if well dried, can be stored all winter long in airy bins or gunny sacks. As needed, ears can be broken in half and thrown to the geese to shell for themselves. If sown in the late summer or early fall, wheat, rye, barley and rape will supply fall and early spring grazing, and then the following summer and fall when the seeds are mature, geese can be turned into the grain patch for half an hour or so each day to harvest their own meal. Kafir and milo produce large seed heads that can be hand-harvested and stored or fed whole.

Besides grains, there is a whole array of leaf, root and vining crops that will add variety and nutrients to your birds' diets. Especially valuable is produce that can be stored for winter feeding when vitamin-rich grasses are dormant. Geese enjoy and benefit from most of the same vegetables you and I relish, so use your imagination when planting for your birds. Some crops I would suggest are summer and winter squash, Swiss Chard, kale, spinach, cabbage, potatoes, carrots, parsnips, turnips, sugar beets and mangels.

A large assortment of natural crops are also available for planting in and around bodies of water. Some of the favorites of geese include wild celery, wild rice and wild millet. The following are nurseries specializing in natural game bird crops: Wildlife Nurseries, P.O. Box 2724-F, Oshkosh, WI 54901; and Kester's Wild Game Food Nurseries, Inc., P.O. Box V-a, Omro, WI 54963.

Grit and Calcium

Wild geese visit sandbars at regular intervals where they pick up sand and small gravel to give their gizzards "teeth" for grinding tough seeds and grasses. To utilize their feed efficiently, domestic birds also need grinding stones, and if grit isn't available naturally, granite grit, coarse sand or small pea-sized gravel should be provided free choice at all times in a container separate from their feed.

If your birds have not had a source of grit for a period of time, introduce it to them gradually — approximately one heaping teaspoon per bird every other day for the first week — to prevent them from over indulging and becoming, quite literally, stoned. (See Hardware Disease and Esophagus Impaction, Chapter 11.) Because geese will pick up almost anything in their search for grit, avoid running them in areas where there is junk, such as old nails, broken glass and pieces of metal. One goosekeeper reported that he has removed live 22-caliber bullets, marbles and dimes from the gizzards of butchered geese.

During much of the year, mature geese ingest all the calcium they need through the grass and grains they consume. However, when females are expected to lay more than one small clutch of eggs, they need to have their diets supplemented with calcium several weeks prior to and throughout the laying season if good shell quality is expected. Prepared laying feeds normally contain sufficient calcium, but when using grains or home mixes, a calcium-rich product such as oyster shells or crushed dried egg shells should be fed free choice. It is possible for laying rations — especially those prepared for chickens — to have too much calcium which can result in thick egg shells that are difficult for goslings to crack and exit. Calcium recommendations for goose breeder rations are 2.25 to 2.75 percent, although some breeders feel that anything over 2.5 percent is excessive. One hatchery reported a significant improvement in the hatchability of their goose eggs after lowering the calcium content of the ration from above 3 percent to 2.5 percent.

FEEDERS

To reduce waste and the possibility of contaminated feed, it is best to serve geese their meals in clean feeders rather than on the ground. A variety of dining ware can be used: dishpans, buckets, hanging tube feeders or a popular old standby, the V-shaped wooden trough. Feeders should be difficult for the birds to tip over, but easy for you to dump out for cleaning. When your geese are on a limited grain or mixed feed diet, provide sufficient feeding space so that all birds can get their portion without excessive crowding. For each light to mediumweight goose, allow approximately eight to ten lineal inches of trough

Chopped green feed, corn stalks, spent bean plants, leafy hay, silage and other plant materials are best utilized if fed from a rack feeder or manger.

space, and twelve to fourteen inches for heavyweights. To keep birds from trampling and soiling cut or chopped green feed such as lawn clippings, corn stalks and spent bean plants, we use a rack feeder or manger that is located under a roof or tree for shade which slows wilting.

FINISHING ROASTING GEESE

If goslings have been on pasture during much of the growing period and fed limited quantities of concentrated feed or grains, a finishing period of heavy feeding and limited exercise will result in a larger carcass and meat that is tender and juicy. For three to four weeks prior to butchering, the birds should be supplied non-medicated finishing pellets (such as for broiler chickens or turkeys) or grains free choice, and penned in a clean, shady plot or small pasture where they have a constant supply of drinking water.

Geese fatten the best in cool weather, and are easier and more pleasant to pluck if their plumage is unsoiled and in full feather. Young geese are usually the least pinny between the ages of nine to eleven weeks, fifteen to seventeen weeks, and again at twenty-two to twenty-six weeks, so the finishing period should be planned accordingly. Due to their strong social attachments, geese will often stop eating for a few days and lose weight if only one or a few birds are removed from a flock or penned separately for the finishing period.

BREEDING YEARLING GEESE

Like many facets of poultry breeding and management, the question of whether year-old geese can be expected to produce goslings can't be

TABLE 17   FERTILITY AND HATCHABILITY OF EGGS LAID BY SEVEN
YEARLING PILGRIM GEESE

Date Set	# of Eggs Set	# of Eggs Fertile	% of Eggs Fertile	# of Goslings Hatched	Hatch of All Eggs	Hatch of Fertile Eggs
February 28	25	23	92%	5	20%	22%
March 7	30	27	90%	7	23%	26%
March 18	32	31	97%	11	34%	35%
April 1	31	31	100%	18	58%	58%
April 14	41	36	88%	28	68%	78%
April 29	29	28	97%	24	83%	86%
Totals	188	176	94%	93	49%	53%

Note: Most breeders report hatchability patterns for eggs produced by yearlings similar to the above,
with poor hatches early, but improved results later in the season. However, one major U.S. hatchery
reports that the smaller early season eggs produced by their yearling stock hatch better than the large
eggs laid early in the year by their aged geese.

answered with a simple yes or no. The ability of yearlings to reproduce depends
on breed, strain and the care they receive. Species such as Canada and Egyptian
seldom breed before their third year, and Dewlap Toulouse often cannot be
relied upon as breeders until they are two or three years old. Except for some
strains that are highly inbred, well-grown yearlings of most other domestic
varieties reproduce satisfactorily, if they are managed properly.

To obtain consistently good results with yearlings, they must be supplied
adequate amounts of feed (see Table 9) as goslings and during their first fall and
winter so they will be well-developed and in good condition when the
breeding season rolls around. Birds that are forced to forage most of their food
as goslings and brought through the winter in poor flesh seldom breed successfully their first year. To improve egg size, hatchability and gosling vigor, yearlings should be fed a ration that is well fortified with vitamins and minerals and
that contains 18 to 20 percent protein, one month prior to and throughout the
laying season.

In several studies on the productivity of yearling geese, it has been found
that while fertility is fairly consistent throughout the laying season, the hatchability of eggs produced by a yearling flock typically starts out low but improves as the season progresses. While Table 17 gives the record of a small flock
of yearling Pilgrims, similar results have been obtained in larger groups of year-
old Embden, Toulouse and Chinese geese. Because hatchability normally is
low, some breeders feel it is impractical to incubate the first six to eight eggs
laid by yearling geese. When year-old geese are allowed to incubate their own
eggs, I suggest that the first clutch be removed, encouraging the goose to lay a
second nest-full which should hatch better.

MANAGING LAYING GEESE

It is a common practice for people who keep a small flock of geese to allow
their birds to lay a nest of eggs and then incubate them naturally. Under such
conditions, geese need little special care in the spring other than a shady

TABLE 18   TYPICAL EFFECTS OF MANAGEMENT ON EGG PRODUCTION

Treatment	Annual Egg Production per Goose	
	White Chinese	Production Toulouse
No grain or pellets provided Given access to pasture Exposed to natural day length	14-20	6-9
Fed grains Given access to pasture Exposed to natural day length	22-36	12-18
Fed 18% protein laying pellets Given access to pasture Artificial lighting schedule	60-100	35-40

nesting site, an ample supply of clean nesting material, such as straw or dried grass, and protection from predators. However, if you desire the maximum number of eggs for hatching or eating purposes, several management practices can be used which will triple or quadruple the natural production of each goose.

Geese are primarily spring layers. If adequately fed in mild climates, they often begin laying the first part of February or earlier, but in cold northern areas, production is usually delayed until late February or early March unless lights are used. Geese typically lay every other day although some females will ovulate two or more days in succession. Unlike their next of kin, the domestic ducks who nearly always deposit their eggs in the early morning, geese lay throughout the day. The length and intensity of the laying season depends a great deal on breed, age of the females, management and climate. Peak production is reached during moderately cool weather, and normally slacks off soon after the mercury consistently climbs to 80° F (27° C) or higher during the daytime.

During the breeding season, geese are extremely sensitive to sudden changes in their environment and diet. To prevent low fertility and discontinued egg production, breeding geese must not: 1) have their diet changed; 2) be left without drinking water; 3) have a sudden change in the amount of daylight they receive; 4) be exposed to drastic temperature fluctuation; or 5) be repeatedly frightened or chased to exhaustion.

Lighting

Day length is a major influence in the natural control of the reproductive cycle in birds. Short days and decreasing length of daylight, such as experienced in the fall and winter months in North America, automatically slow down the reproductive organs of both male and female fowl. Conversely, the longer days and increasing day lengths of spring stimulate males to mate and females to lay. While geese have yet to come close to the productivity of egg-bred ducks, chickens or coturnix quail, they can be induced to lay earlier and longer if an appropriate lighting schedule is carefully followed.

TABLE 19   IDENTIFYING PROBLEMS IN THE LAYING FLOCK

Symptoms	Common Causes
Thin or soft-shelled eggs	Usually a vitamin D3 deficiency; also high temperatures, abnormal reproductive organs or calcium deficiency.
Under or oversized, odd-shaped eggs	Temporary malfunction of the reproductive organs; yearling geese; in some cases, abnormal oviducts.
Blood on shell's exterior	Ruptured blood vessel at the cloaca opening or an infected vent; frequently occurs when young geese begin laying.
Geese with back of head and neck bare of feathers; in extreme cases, skin is raw or scabby	Too many ganders, resulting in excessive mating activity; ganders sometimes have favorite geese they mate with repeatedly.
Geese prematurely stop laying and/or molt	Sudden change in diet or lighting schedule; birds frequently left without drinking water; moving birds to unfamiliar quarters; birds repeatedly frightened or run to exhaustion; an unseasonably hot spell.
Prolapsed oviduct and broken down abdomen	Poor muscle tone due to obesity, high egg production, old age or inherited weakness; bird straining to lay oversized egg.

Geese are sensitive to changes in the amount of light they receive. Once production commences, it is vital that the length of daylight never decreases, or the rate of lay and fertility will be severely curtailed. A reduction of only one hour per twenty-four hour period for several days can negatively effect heavily producing geese. Excessive exposure to light is also undesirable since it can result in premature molting or broodiness — sixteen hours of light daily seems to be near the upper limit.

Few people have the schedule or discipline to manually turn lights on and off on a precise schedule every day throughout the laying season, and this method is not recommended. By using an automatic timer that turns lights on before daybreak and off after nightfall, geese can be exposed to a constant, carefully controlled lighting routine.

During the fall or winter, geese normally commence laying four to five weeks after a lighting schedule is started. For the production of hatching eggs, it is undesirable to bring geese into production too fast since a minimum of four to six weeks of lighting is usually required before ganders become sexually active. Hatching eggs are seldom desired before the first of February, so it is questionable whether it is advisable to commence artificial lighting on breeding flocks much before the first of the year. Chinese of some strains will lay for an extended season of six to seven months or longer in cool weather, so for the production of eating eggs (or for hatching if there is a need) these birds can be put on a lighting schedule in early fall.

The light intensity needed to stimulate egg production is relatively low (approximately one foot-candle at ground level, which equals about one bulb watt per four square feet of floorspace when the light bulb is mounted at a height of eight feet). One forty- to sixty-watt incandescent bulb hung six to eight feet high will provide sufficient lighting for 150 to 250 square feet of floorspace when geese are confined to a building. For outside yards, a 100-watt bulb with reflector will give adequate illumination for 300 to 400 square feet.

The amount of light young geese are exposed to needs to be watched to prevent premature egg production. If young females are exposed to excessive light (more than fourteen hours per twenty-four hour period) or increasing day lengths between the ages of sixteen to thirty weeks, they may lay out of season and before their bodies are adequately mature. When exposed to all-night security lights, I have seen well-fed Toulouse, Pilgrim and Chinese geese begin laying at the age of five to six months. Premature laying before eight to ten months of age is undesirable since it can result in stunted growth, strained reproductive organs and lowered production in the future.

We use the following lighting schedule with good success on our breeding geese, and I recommend it as a guideline if you desire maximum egg production and good fertility. When setting up your own lighting scheme, keep in mind that excessive light seems to shorten the breeding season by causing premature broodiness and molting.

Time Period	*Hours of Light Daily*
1st week of artificial lighting (about the first of January)	Add sufficient light so geese are receiving 11½ hours of total light (natural + artificial) daily.
2nd, 3rd and 4th weeks	Add 20 minutes weekly (in two 10-minute jumps) so by end of 4th week 12½ total hours have been reached.
5th week and after	Add 15 minutes weekly until 15 to 16 hours of total light daily is reached. Maintain at this level until geese stop laying.

Breaking Up Broody Geese

Geese of most breeds lay a clutch of five to twelve eggs and then get the urge to set on them. Once they become broody, egg production soon stops. However, broodiness can often be delayed if eggs are gathered daily and dummy eggs are not left in the nest. When geese do go broody, they can often be stimulated back into production by isolating them in a well-lit pen or yard devoid of nests and dark corners. After five to eight days of isolation, geese will normally lose their maternal desires and can be returned to the flock.

CULLING BREEDING STOCK

Not all goslings that hatch develop into mature birds that are suitable for use as breeders. In nature, predators and harsh living conditions cull out the weak and deformed specimens. Under domestication, geese lead a pampered life and unworthy individuals must be weeded out to maintain the vigor and productivity of a flock.

When choosing potential breeders, only birds displaying robust health, strong legs, freedom from deformities and adequate body size should be retained. If you are breeding purebred geese, proper size, shape, carriage, color and markings should also be considered. (See Chapter 5 for specific suggestions on selecting breeding stock for each breed.)

While geese have been known to reproduce twenty years or longer, breeding stock normally should be replaced after three to five years if the highest level of productivity is desired. In most breeds, the female's best egg-producing years are two through four, with one and five being about equal. Production usually drops significantly after the fifth year. Ganders seem to be the most fertile their second and third years, dropping off about 20 percent their fourth year — with the first and fifth years being similar.

Well grown and in good feather condition, this five-month-old African exhibits the vigor that is desired in young breeding stock of any breed.

The following deformities and weaknesses show up from time to time in geese, and most — if not all — are highly inheritable. I strongly suggest that birds with any of these faults not be used for reproduction purposes. Some defects are recessive or masked over in the first generation, but then crop up with increasing frequency in subsequent generations.

Drooping Shoulders — Occasionally geese are seen that walk or stand in a hunched position with their shoulders carried unnaturally low — a sure sign of low vitality and fertility.

Abnormal Sex Organs — Females with abnormally distended or broken down abdomens often are not dependable egg producers and are prone to prolapsed oviducts (see page 137). Adult ganders occasionally lose the ability to retract their penis (see page 138) which may cause the sex organ to shrivel and become useless or drop off. Poor feeds, such as moldy or blighted grains, can severely affect the development of a gander's penis and render him useless as a breeder. To insure good fertility, ganders should be vent sexed after each breeding season to guarantee that their equipment is in good working order.

Weak Legs — A diet deficiency is often the cause of this problem (see page 134), although weak legs can also be inherited. Genetic leg weakness is usually marked by birds whose legs give out after walking or running short distances.

Crooked Toes — This disfigurement is easy to identify by one or more toes that are bent sharply at an unnatural angle.

Slipped Wing — The tip of a slipped wing is twisted at the wrist joint, causing the flight feathers to protrude from the bird's body rather than folding smoothly against the back (see page 140).

Wry Tail — Wry tails are the result of a muscle or bone deformity and are constantly cocked to one side rather than pointing straight back.

Crooked and Roach Backs — These conditions are the result of malformed spinal columns that either cause the back to be curved from side to side when viewed from above, or humped and shortened when viewed from the side. In mild cases, these problems may not be noticeable until the bird is caught and a hand is run over the back. Roach backs are most often seen in Chinese geese, while crooked spines are more common in the heavyweight breeds.

Kinked and Bowed Necks — Necks with an obvious crook in them are usually inherited, but occasionally are the result of an injury or from keeping birds in a low box for an extended period of time. Excessively bowed necks are uncommon, but occasionally seen in Chinese and African geese.

Crossed Bill — In crossed bills, the upper and/or lower half of the bill is twisted to the side, and the two mandibles are not aligned — sometimes evident at hatching although it usually does not show up until the bird is older.

Blindness — A few strains of geese (especially those that are inbred) show a high incidence of clouded pupils. While some goslings exhibit this blinding fault upon hatching, in other birds it does not develop until later.

Undesirable Weaknesses and Deformities

kinked neck

bowed neck

wry tail

drooping shoulders

slipped wings

CATCHING AND HOLDING GEESE

For your own well-being and that of the goose, care must be used when catching and holding these strapping birds. Geese are amazingly strong, and if they are not handled properly, you can be soundly pounded with their wings, bit with their bill or scratched by their claws, and they can be injured in their vigorous struggle to free themselves from your grasp.

When catching, avoid pursuing geese across rough ground or where they are likely to collide with feeders or other rigid objects. Rather than having a wild goose chase around a large pen or pasture, it is helpful to walk the birds into a small catch pen or V-shaped corner.

To avoid lame birds due to disjointed or broken legs, geese must not be grabbed or held by their legs. Rather, you should grasp them securely — but gently — by the neck, just below the head. At this point, the snared bird, depending on its mood or personality, will either try to pull away by backing up, or, if aggressive or badly frightened, it may turn towards you and attempt to flog you with its wing butts. If you've latched onto a backer, slide your free hand under the body and secure both legs between your thumb and first finger. Lifting the captive from the ground, its weight should be resting on your forearm with its head pointed back where it won't be able to peck your eyes or

Andrea Peterson and her Sebastopol demonstrate how geese should be caught and held, so as not to injure the birds' legs.

grab your nose or a lip — all of which geese have been known to do! The bird's wings should be pinned firmly between your body and forearm.

Now, if you've tangled with a flogger, there are two courses of action available — one, decide you really didn't need to catch the rascal and turn it loose; or, two, if you're sure this particular bird must be captured, with your free hand deftly grasp both wings just above where they connect to the bird's body. Transport the bird with its weight distributed between the wings and neck. Most fowl literature warns never to carry birds by their wings, but realistically, this method is the only practical way to transport some geese without sustaining heavy blows from their pinions.

Geese that are tame and accustomed to being handled can often be picked up simply by placing a hand on either side of the body. However, no matter how friendly the goose, it's always a sound practice to keep the bird's head away from the face and to point the tail end away from yourself or any companions to avoid unnecessarily fertilizing anyone.

DEALING WITH AGGRESSIVE GEESE

It is the exception rather than the rule for geese to be aggressive, excluding the breeding season when they become protective of their nesting territory and goslings. However, individual birds — especially when raised in small flocks — can develop belligerent dispositions and make pests of themselves by biting or beating anyone that approaches too closely or enters their enclosures. This problem is often — but not always — the result of geese being teased and harassed, and can usually be avoided by working quietly among the birds and never making threatening advances towards them. It also seems that overly tamed geese sometimes lose all respect for humans and attempt to dominate them.

Rehabilitating a quarrelsome goose requires an understanding of their nature and sometimes, a heap of patience. People often aggravate the problem either by striking at pursuing birds or beating a hasty retreat. The first action challenges the goose to fight harder, while running away builds the bird's confidence in its ability to chase intruders out of its domain. In working around birds of most sizes, including chickens, geese, swans and emus, I have found that when a bird makes threatening advances, the best strategy is to stand still or quietly go about one's business, being careful not to make sudden moves, or — and this is important — not to turn one's back to the aggressor and appear to be retreating. A sudden motion can be interpreted by birds as a threat while a turned back is taken as an indication of fear, giving the feathered creature confidence to carry out an attack from the rear flanks.

While some people find the stop-and-wait advice hard to follow, this method — with few exceptions — has worked for me over the past twenty years. Lacking a stimulus to fight, aggressive birds usually lose interest quickly and go on their way. Occasionally geese are found that seem to be cantankerous to the core and refuse to relent. If you should run into such a character, you'll have to decide who's going to rule the roost — you or the goose.

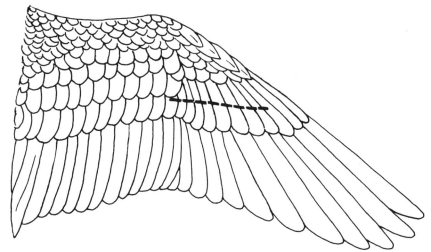

Flying geese can be grounded by clipping the ten primary flight feathers of one wing.

KEEPING FLYING GEESE GROUNDED

To keep flying geese from gliding over fences, it is often necessary to clip one wing of each bird. This operation is performed by cutting the primary flight feathers of one wing using a tin shears or heavy-duty scissors. The secondary wing feathers should be left intact to provide protection from rain and cold temperatures. The two outermost flight feathers can be left uncut so the bird does not appear lopsided. Waterfowl molt their wing feathers and replace them once a year. To keep geese grounded, their wings must be trimmed annually, although domestic breeds such as production Toulouse, American Buffs and Pilgrims often lose most of their desire or ability to fly after they're a year old.

CHAPTER 10

Sexing

The time-honored adage of "what's good for the goose is good for the gander" may very well be true, but there are a lot of goosekeepers, especially newcomers, who have a tough time recognizing which is the goose and which the gander. Unlike ducks and chickens, geese of most varieties lack obvious characteristics — such as distinctive voices, feathering or color — that readily distinguish the hes from the shes. To breed geese successfully, however, one must be able to identify the gender of each bird so that the correct ratio of males to females can be maintained in the breeding flock. Occasionally people tell me that they've had a mating of geese for two, three or more years without the birds ever reproducing. Invariably, after taking a look at the gaggle, the lack of success is apparent — all the birds are the same sex.

To my knowledge, the following methods are the most trustworthy procedures for sexing geese of all ages.

VENT SEXING

The only sure way to sex geese of all ages and breeds is by examining the cloaca. Despite the fact that this procedure is fairly simple to learn and extremely useful, it is surprising how few people have taken the time to learn the technique.

While it is easier to vent sex waterfowl than land fowl, this procedure still requires practice, a basic understanding of the bird's physiology, and care to avoid permanent injury to the bird. If possible, I recommend that you have a knowledgeable waterfowl breeder show you how to vent sex geese before try-ing it yourself. At its best, a written account on sexing is a poor substitute for a firsthand demonstration by an experienced sexer.

Even though geese of all ages can be vent sexed, I suggest that the begin-ner practice on goslings within two or three days after they hatch. While gos-lings of this age are tender and must be handled carefully, they are easily held and their sex organs are readily exposed and sufficiently prominent to be iden-tified with relative ease. Due to the position of their vents, the European breeds normally are easier to sex than Chinese and Africans. As birds mature, the sphincter muscles which surround the vent strengthen, making it more difficult to invert the cloaca and unsheathe the sex organs.

When vent sexing geese, there are four important points you should always keep in mind:

- The abdomen region of newly hatched goslings is extremely delicate and clumsy fingers can kill or permanently injure the bird.

- When sexing live waterfowl of any age, one must never attempt to reveal the sex organs by squeezing or pinching the sides of the vent; but rather, to avoid injuring the bird, the cloaca is rolled open by applying pressure firmly, but gently, down and out on each side and behind the vent.

- A bird has not been sexed until the cloaca has been fully exposed. Peo-ple sometimes assume that a bird is a female if they can't see a penis after applying a little pressure to the sides of the vent. In actuality, a bird can-not positively be identified as a goose until the cloaca has been inverted sufficiently to expose the female genital eminence.

- While the sex organs of goslings are not as difficult to spot as those of ducklings, for accuracy it is essential that these birds are sexed under good lighting.

After studying the accompanying illustrations, with practice you should be able to sex geese of all ages if the following steps are carefully performed. There are several methods for holding goslings and adult geese for sexing. While I'll describe only the procedures I find most comfortable and speedy, you should feel free to experiment. If you're left-handed, the instructions for which finger or hand to use should be reversed.

Step 1—Hold the bird upside down with its head pointed back towards yourself. If the goose is large, its neck can be held between your legs, or if you're seated, the bird can be held under the left arm and its tail bent over your left leg.

Step 2—Using the middle fingers of your right hand, bend the tail to a position where it is almost touching the bird's back.

Step 3—Push the fuzz or feathers surrounding the vent out of the way so you have an unobstructed view of the cloaca.

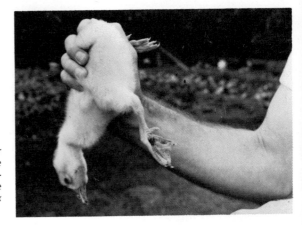

Vent sex goslings under good lighting. Hold the bird head down and double its tail back with one of your middle or index fingers.

Position your thumbs on opposite edges of the vent and place the free index finger just behind the vent. To invert the cloaca, firmly — but gently — apply pressure down and out simultaneously with the thumbs and index finger.

In male goslings, a small light pinkish yellow penis should be visible near the center of the cloaca.

In female goslings, there is a tiny, usually grayish-colored genital eminence in place of the male organ.

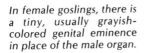

A convenient method for restraining large geese for sexing is to turn the bird up-side-down and hold its neck between your legs.

After bending the tail down and pushing aside the feathers surrounding the vent, position your thumbs on the sides and an index finger on the back of the vent, applying pressure down and out to invert the cloaca.

This is the penis of a virile, mature gander. The organs of sterile males are often withered, dark-colored or atrophed.

Step 4—Holding your thumbs close together, place one on each side of the vent and firmly — but gently — apply pressure down and out. (In adult birds, prior to Step 4, it is often helpful if the sphincter muscles are relaxed by inserting a vaseline coated finger one-half inch into the vent, moving it in a circular motion half a dozen turns.)

Step 5—With the index finger of your right hand, apply pressure down and out on the backside of the vent. This action should invert the cloaca and expose the sex organs.

If it's a gander, a corkscrew-shaped penis will pop up near the center of the cloaca when the vent is inverted. In young males the penis is small and often pale-colored, while in sexually active ganders the organ can be two inches or more in length and deeper-colored.

If it's a goose, no penis will be present when the cloaca is fully inverted. However, a female genital eminence that resembles an undeveloped penis should be visible near the lower edge of the vent opening. This small, usually gray (yellowish in White Chinese) protuberance is more readily seen in geese than in ducks, and should not be confused with the larger and lighter colored penis of the male.

If you have difficulty — The problem most commonly encountered when sexing waterfowl is getting the cloaca inverted sufficiently. If you have this difficulty, check to make sure that

- You have the bird's tail bent back as in the illustrations.

- You are applying pressure down and out simultaneously with both of your thumbs and the right index finger.

Some individual birds naturally are more difficult to sex, so if you have trouble, try a different goose or even a bird of a different age. Don't give up if you get discouraged on your initial attempts. Speed and accuracy in vent sexing will improve with practice. Because the genital eminence of female geese is easily seen, experienced goose sexers can expect nearly 100 percent accuracy.

SEXING BY COLOR

Pilgrims are the only breed that can positively be sexed by color both as goslings and as adults. Newly hatched Pilgrim males have silver-gray down and light-colored bills and feet, while females have darker gray coats, bills and feet. At maturity, ganders are white, often with some gray in the wings, on the rump and in the thigh coverts, while geese are gray with some white on the head and neck.

Pilgrims can be sexed at any age by the color of their down or feathers. In this pair of day-olds, the darker female is on the right and the lighter male on the left.

With their color coded plumage, Pilgrims from pure stock take any guesswork out of sexing. Adult ganders are mostly white, while geese are gray.

For approximately the first month after hatching, most Embden goslings can be sexed by the color of their down. In this pair of four-day-olds, the darker female is on the left, the lighter male on the right.

Embden (and apparently White Sebastopol and Tufted Roman) goslings in the downy stage can also be sexed by down color (males having lighter gray markings than females) until dilution genes fade their plumage. While many so-called Embdens sold by commercial hatcheries are actually crossbreeds and cannot always be sexed by this method, I have yet to see goslings from authentic Embdens that could not be sexed with accuracy by down color.

SEXING BY CARRIAGE AND BODY SIZE

Generally within each breed, ganders are larger, have longer and thicker necks, bolder heads, less developed abdomens and carry their heads and shoulders higher than the more refined geese. In a mature flock containing birds of the same breed and strain, experienced goosekeepers can usually distinguish the gender of individual birds by the above secondary sex characteristics. However, flocks made up of several ages, breeds or even different strains of the same breed can have such a wide variety of traits that the above characteristics cannot always be depended upon for accurate sexing.

In a flock consisting of birds of the same age and breed, males normally are larger, taller and coarser than females. In this group of yearling Brown Chinese, the three ganders are easily picked out by their larger body size, longer necks and more prominent forehead knobs.

SEXING BY KNOB SIZE

In Africans and Chinese, the knobs of ganders normally develop earlier and substantially larger than those of geese. However, knob size varies a great deal both among various strains and individual birds, so length of neck, body size and carriage should also be taken into consideration when sexing these breeds by secondary sex characteristics.

SEXING BY VOICE

I know several waterfowl breeders who can identify the gender of geese with amazing accuracy simply by listening to the bird's voice. My ears are not sensitive enough to consistently pick up the unique calls of males and females, particularly when dealing with a large flock of conversing birds. However, if you have a good ear, with practice you probably can develop this skill. Sexually mature ganders of the European breeds typically possess higher pitched voices than geese, just the opposite of what's normal for humans.

CHAPTER 11

Health and Physical Problems

Geese that are raised in small flocks are seldom bothered with serious illnesses, even when given a minimum of care. However, in spite of the tremendous hardiness and disease resistance of these waterfowl, wise is the goose-keeper that practices the established truism that "prevention is the best cure." When troubles do arise, they can nearly always be traced to a deficient diet, stagnant water, moldy bedding, medicated feed or overcrowded and filthy living conditions.

Should trouble arise and you are unable to diagnose the malady, promptly seek advice from an experienced waterfowl breeder, veterinarian or animal diagnostic laboratory. Procrastination in the treatment of an ailing bird may prove fatal and can result in an epidemic. When using medications, be sure to give the correct dosage for the entire length of time recommended — even if the birds appear to be cured earlier. Premature termination of treatment often results in a relapse.

Sick or injured geese should be penned in a dry, clean enclosure, and provided a balanced diet and clean drinking water. However, to prevent them from becoming frantic and refusing food, they should not — as a rule — be isolated from their mate. Dead birds should always be removed as quickly as possible to avoid the possibility of attracting predators and, in the case of communicable diseases, to curb the likelihood of infecting healthy birds. Burn carcasses in an incinerator or bury them deep enough that they will not be dug up by scavengers. Leaving deceased birds laying around or tossing them over the fence into the bushes is an open invitation for trouble.

DISEASES, PHYSICAL DISORDERS AND PARASITES

Of the following ailments, those marked with an asterisk are the most commonly seen disorders in small goose flocks, the majority of which can be diagnosed and treated at home.

Aspergillosis

Causes — Commonly known as brooder pneumonia, this disease is the result of Aspergillosis fumigatus mold being inhaled into the lungs when goslings are hatched in contaminated incubators or from being brooded on moldy bedding or fed moldy feed.

Symptoms — Aspergillosis is normally a disease of young goslings and indicated by gasping or labored breathing, poor appetite, general weakness and occasionally is accompanied by sticky eyes. The lungs of affected birds often contain small yellowish nodules about the size of a BB shot. Goslings are the most susceptible the first few days after hatching.

Treatment — There is no known cure, but to prevent it from spreading, infected birds should be destroyed, the brooding area and equipment disinfected, and the feed and bedding checked for musty odor or visible signs of mold.

Prevention — Hatch eggs only in thoroughly disinfected incubators and use mold-free bedding and feed. In some situations, particularly in warm, humid climates, it may be necessary to fumigate the eggs and hatching compartment of the incubator shortly prior to the hatch date (see Fumigation, Chapter 7).

Botulism

Causes — This deadly food poisoning, colloquially known as limberneck, is caused by a toxin produced by Clostridium botulinum bacteria which is commonly found in soil, spoiled food and decaying animal and plant matter. Botulism strikes most frequently when the weather has been dry and water levels in ponds and lakes drop, leaving decaying plants and animals exposed where the geese find and eat them. Maggots that feed on decaying carcasses often carry the botulism toxin. Geese can also contract this toxicant from spoiled feed or canned food from the pantry.

Symptoms — A few hours after eating poisoned food, birds may lose control of their leg, wing and neck muscles. In some cases, body feathers loosen and are easily extracted. Geese that are swimming when paralysis of the neck develops often drown before they are able to climb out on land. Dying birds may slip into a coma several hours before expiring. Botulism normally kills in three to twenty-four hours, although in mild cases birds may recover in several days.

Treatment — All geese that are suspected of having eaten poisoned food should be confined to a clean, shady yard or building and immediately provided fresh drinking water with a laxative — either one pint of molasses or one pound of epsom salts per five gallons water — added to it for four hours. Birds that cannot drink on their own should be treated individually. The addition of one part potassium to 3,000 parts drinking water or individual doses of one teaspoon castor oil have also been recommended as treatments. On birds that are particularly valuable, it is helpful to flush out the contents of the esophagus with warm water by using a funnel and rubber tube which is inserted into the mouth and down the esophagus several inches. Every effort must be made to locate the source of the poisoning so that further problems can be avoided. A vaccine has been developed, but it is rather expensive and often difficult to obtain on short notice.

Prevention — Bury or burn carcasses of dead animals and clean up rotting vegetation. Do not let your geese feed in stagnant bodies of water during dry periods nor give the birds spoiled canned goods or feed.

Broken Bones

The bones of birds have a wonderful ability to mend themselves. However, to prevent a goose from being permanently disfigured or crippled, it is often helpful to set and immobilize a wing or leg that is fractured.

Setting — Broken bones should be treated promptly, preferably within twenty-four hours after the accident. A bone is set by gently pulling apart, and if necessary, slightly twisting the two halves until they mesh properly.

Splints — To heal properly, broken bones should be held in alignment with splints (popsicle or tongue sticks work satisfactorily in many cases). A rigid support should be positioned on either side and as far above and below the fracture as possible, and held securely in place with strong tape. The patient should be frequently checked to insure that the brace is staying in place and that blood circulation is not being restricted. Splints can normally be removed in fourteen to twenty-eight days.

Cannibalism

Causes — Few vices of birds are more disgusting than when they eat one another's feathers and flesh. However, this problem — especially in geese — is usually brought on by improper management. For survival, goslings hatch with a strong instinct to nibble on objects around them. When brooded artificially in confinement without pasture or chopped green feed, young goslings satisfy their instincts by pulling on each other's wings, tails and down of the back. If allowed to go unchecked, some individuals will be partially denuded, blood will be drawn and holes may be eaten in the flesh. Cannibalism is intensified by high brooding temperatures, excessive light, overcrowding, a diet low in fiber, insufficient quantities of food and pelleted feeds.

Symptoms — Goslings show wet, bare and bloody areas, typically on the wings, tail and back.

Treatment — At the first indication of feather eating, check brooder temperature, reduce the intensity of light (using colored bulbs — especially blue — often helps), and provide birds with sufficient space, a balanced diet, adequate quantities of feed and tender green foods such as grass, clover, dandelion, chard and kale. If greens are not available, mold-free, leafy hay can usually be substituted. Anti-pick lotions and salves are available and sometimes are helpful if used promptly.

Prevention — Correct brooding temperature; dim, colored lights; sufficient floorspace; a balanced diet; the daily feeding of greens or roughage and putting goslings on pasture as soon as feasible normally eliminate this bothersome and sometimes serious problem.

Choking

While eating, geese will occasionally get feed caught in the back of their throats, which can block their breathing. Normally, after a vigorous shaking of the head, the passageway is cleared and breathing returns to normal. However, sometimes a bird is unable to clear its throat and will suffocate if not promptly aided. When a goose obviously needs your assistance, pull its head forward until it is in a straight line with the neck, pry open the bill, and push your finger, a piece of ½-inch rubber tubing or the eraser end of a new pencil down the bird's throat until the obstruction is dislodged.

Coccidiosis

Causes — Geese are often considered immune to coccidiosis, but when brooded on litter in damp, filthy quarters, goslings can suffer serious infestations. This major poultry disease is caused by Coccidia, a one-celled parasite. These microscopic organisms attack and destroy cells in various portions of the digestive tract. There are numerous known species, but only a few infect geese. Coccidia are generally present in moderate numbers wherever birds are raised, and they can survive in soil for more than a year. However, this disease seldom causes problems in geese unless it is invited by poor sanitation. The egglike oocyst produced by Coccidia can be transported from one location to another by various means such as on the shoes or clothing of people, in the droppings of wild birds and by purchasing infected fowl.

Symptoms — In general, symptoms include reduced appetite, ruffled feathers, heads drawn close to the body, and sometimes diarrhea and bloody droppings. In chronic cases, birds may grow slowly and never attain full size or production or waste away and finally die. In severe outbreaks, large numbers of goslings may die within a week or less. Because internal symptoms depend on the species of Coccidia, it is recommended that birds be taken to a diagnostic lab to confirm coccidiosis outbreaks.

Treatment — Normally, sulfa medications and coccidiostats manufactured for chickens and turkeys will also be effective for geese. These preparations can be added to feed or drinking water and are usually available from feedstores and poultry supply dealers. However, the recommended dosages for chickens and turkeys should be reduced by approximately one-third to one-half for geese since waterfowl consume greater quantities of feed and water and over-doses of these drugs can be deadly.

Prevention — To thrive, Coccidia need filthy bedding that is damp and sufficiently warm. The best prevention therefore, is dry, clean bedding that is turned or changed frequently to promote dryness; or better yet, wire floors in the brooding area, or at least under and around the watering containers.

Cuts and Wounds

Compared to most other animals, the normal body temperature of our feathered friends is feverishly high (104° to 109° F or 40° to 43° C), which provides extra protection against most infections. When geese are kept in reasonably sanitary surroundings, superficial scratches and abrasions normally heal without treatment. However, when a goose sustains an open wound or is badly mauled by a predator, clinical care is needed. After catching, but prior to working on an injured patient, always wash your hands thoroughly with hot, soapy water.

Treating Open Wounds — Deep or jagged cuts should usually have the feathers trimmed away from the edges — always hold a clean piece of gauze or lintless cloth over the wound while trimming feathers to prevent bits of web-bing from adhering to and contaminating the exposed flesh. Wash the wound with warm water to which a mild soap has been added, and then thoroughly rinse with clear, warm water. Small pieces of shredded, loose skin that will not heal can be trimmed away. To speed healing and to prevent infection and the development of maggots, I like to apply a medicated ointment such as Nitrofurazone once daily or every other day. If open cuts are not properly attended, especially during warm weather, infections and maggots can be problematic.

Sewing Up Gaping Wounds — Stitches are sometimes required when large patches of skin have been torn loose or deep lacerations sustained. While suture needles and silk thread are preferred, a sterilized sewing needle and white thread work satisfactorily for surface suturing. Each suture or stitch should be well-anchored in the skin, but not over ⅛ inch deep. Sutures should be spaced approximately ⅜ inch apart and drawn tight enough to bring the two edges of the torn flesh together without much puckering. If non-absorbing thread is used, the stitches should be snipped and pulled out with a tweezers in four to five days. As an extra precaution it is often advisable to treat birds with serious or multiple wounds with oral or injectable antibiotics, such as penicillin or a combination of penicillin and streptomycin. (Streptomycin can be toxic to fowl, so when using this antibiotic on a number of birds, it is a good idea to inject one or two individuals first and observe them for thirty minutes for signs of staggering or drowsiness.)

*Foot Problems

Causes — The bottoms of the feet of waterfowl seem to be more tender than those of land dwelling birds such as chickens. Foot trouble can be the result of geese bruising, cutting or picking up a splinter or thorn in the pads of their feet, or possibly from spending much of their time on dry, hard or sharp gravel surfaces without having access to bathing water. However, a common cause that is frequently overlooked is a dietary deficiency in biotin, pantothenic acid, riboflavin or one of the other vitamins or minerals important in maintaining healthy tissues. Bacterial infections (bumble foot) may also cause foot pad or joint infections, with staphylococal bacteria commonly being involved.

Symptoms — Large corns and calluses develop on the bottoms of feet. In some cases, deep bleeding cracks are present and/or the pads of the feet swell and become infected — known as bumble foot — causing the bird to go lame.

Treatment — If a deficient diet is suspected, supplement the rations with a vitamin premix or feedstuffs (such as brewer's dried yeast, whey, dried skim milk or alfalfa meal) that are rich in vitamin A, biotin, pantothenic acid and riboflavin.

If the ball of the foot is inflamed, wash the foot with warm, soapy water, disinfect with rubbing alcohol, and then remove splinter — if present — or open the pad with a sharp, sterilized instrument. (I have found an exacto knife with a new blade or old-fashioned single-edged razor blade to be useful for this operation.) Remove any pus or hard yellow core, disinfect the incision with alcohol and apply a medicated wound salve such as Nitrofurazone.

Place the patient in a clean pen that is bedded with a deep layer of fresh straw (never sawdust or wood shavings) and provide a balanced ration, green feed and at least a small container of clean bathing water. The daily washing, disinfecting and application of medicated ointment to the wound facilitate healing. For extra valuable birds, a dose of penicillin in tablet form for a minimum of ten to fourteen days seems to be helpful. In stubborn cases a bacteriological culture, isolation of the causative bacteria and an antibiotic sensitivity test may be done by a laboratory.

Prevention — Geese that receive a balanced diet and that are not chased over hard, sharp surfaces seldom develop foot problems. Access to pasture and bathing water reduce its occurrence.

Fowl Cholera

Causes — Fowl cholera is a highly contagious disease of both wild and domestic birds that is caused by the bacterium Pasteurella multocida, which can survive in soil and decaying carcasses for several months or longer. It can be spread by wild birds, rodents and scavengers, or from geese pecking at infected dead birds. Although cholera can occur any time of year, it thrives best in a damp, cool environment.

Symptoms — In waterfowl, cholera often gives little or no warning, with apparently healthy birds dying suddenly. Chronic cases may be signaled by listlessness, lameness, swollen joints, diarrhea, breathing difficulties and increased water consumption.

Waterfowl which die of an acute attack typically show little — if any — sign of the disease upon post mortem examination. In less severe cases, the liver is often streaked with light-colored areas and spotted with minute hemorrhages and gray spots of dead tissue. It is fairly common for there to be tiny red hemorrhages on the intestines, gizzard and heart that are visible to the naked eye. Also, the spleen may be enlarged.

Treatment — Current recommended treatment is one of the following sulfa drugs: Sulfaquinoxaline sodium at the rate of .04 percent in drinking water, or .1 percent in feed for two or three days; Sulfamethazine at .4 percent in feed for three to five days or Sulfamethazine sodium, 12.5 percent solution at thirty ml per gallon of drinking water; or Sulfamerazine sodium at .5 percent in feed for five to seven days. Sulfa drugs must be used with caution, particularly with breeding stock, as they can be toxic. High levels of antibiotics such as tetracycline are sometimes used in the feed or injected under the skin. For the small flock owner, the most practical means of treatment is usually to purchase easy-to-use prepared medications for use in the drinking water, such as Salsbury Sulquin.

Prevention — Sound sanitation practices are the best prevention for fowl cholera. Water containers should be placed over wire-covered platforms, waterers frequently cleaned and occasionally disinfected with sodium hypochlorite (common bleach) or an approved livestock sanitizer. Eliminate stagnant mudholes in the goose yard and burn or deeply bury all carcasses of dead birds and animals. In localities where there is a history of cholera, pasture rotation and vaccination using commercially available bacterins according to the manufacturer's recommendations may be necessary.

Frostbite

Cause — Prolonged exposure of the feet and knobs of geese to extreme cold can result in freezing of tissues.

Symptoms — Birds have their feet frozen to the ground or ice; geese limp when forced to walk; feet show swelling and redness, and feel hot to the touch; and later, tissue that has been frozen sloughs off due to gangrene. The dark knobs of Brown Chinese and African geese that have been frostbit will develop patches of orange. Frostbite often is not detected until lameness, gangrene or discoloration occurs.

Treatment — When waterfowl are found with their feet frozen to ice or the ground, pour warm water that is 90° to 105° F (32° to 40° C) — no hotter — over the frozen parts until they are freed. Then, rapidly warm the frostbitten feet in a water bath (105° to 108° F or 40° to 42° C) for fifteen to twenty minutes, and give the patient lukewarm drinking water. Do not rub the affected parts. If gangrene sets in, the frozen areas may eventually drop off or may need to be amputated and treated as an open wound. The oral administration of antibiotics such as penicillin and terramycin to birds with severe frostbite reduces the chances of infection.

Prevention — Unless waterfowl have access to a large body of open water, geese of all breeds should be inclosed in a yard or shed that is bedded with a thick layer of bedding and provided protection from wind when temperatures fall below 20° F (-7° C).

Hardware Disease and Esophagus Impaction

Causes — Nails, bits of wire, pieces of string, blades of tough grass, excessive quantities of gravel or other hard-to-digest objects are occasionally swallowed by geese. When ingested, these objects sometimes puncture or impact some portion of the upper digestive system.

Common signs of illness in geese include ruffled head fathers, dull eyes and birds that stand or sit by themselves.

Symptoms — In the case of hardware disease, birds slowly lose weight, stop eating and sit around with eyes partially closed, apparently in severe pain. When a post mortem is performed, the hardware is often found lodged in the esophagus or gizzard. Frequently, the foreign object will penetrate the wall, causing peritonitis. With an esophagus impaction, a lump, caused by an obstruction, is often visible in the lower neck.

Treatment — There is no practical remedy for hardware disease. When an esophagus impaction is the problem, the wad of material can often be kneaded loose by gently massaging the compaction from the outside. If relief cannot be achieved by external methods, the blockage may have to be removed surgically.

To prepare for this operation, the feathers directly over the impaction should be plucked, a few at a time, until an area approximately 1½ inches in diameter is exposed. After washing your hands with soap and hot water, swab the plucked patch with rubbing alcohol, gently tighten the skin by stretching it between the thumb and index finger and make a shallow, inch-long incision through the skin with a sterilized (boiled for three minutes) knife — I suggest using an exacto knife with a new blade. A second incision is made through the wall of the esophagus.

Using your finger or a sterilized, blunt instrument, remove the troublesome material from the esophagus and then rinse with clean, warm water. Using a fine needle and gut suture material (gut must be used so that it will dissolve), draw the incised edges of the esophagus together with three or four single stitches that are tied off separately. The outer cut can be sown in a similar manner, except that silk thread should be used. When finished, swab the incision with alcohol, force feed several capsules of codliver oil and provide drinking water — but no feed — for twenty-four hours. Thereafter, supply small quantities of greens and pellets several times daily until the stitches are removed. The outer sutures can be taken out after about a week.

Prevention — Never leave nails, wire or string where birds can reach them, and do not force geese to live on dry, fibrous grass. Unfortunately, it takes only one misplaced nail to cause the death of a valuable bird. Whenever hardware is being used in an area to which birds have access, every effort should be made to retrieve dropped nails and bits of wire or string.

Also it seems advisable not to place large quantities of grit in troughs with feed, or, if geese have been without grit for some time, give only the equivalent of one teaspoonful per bird every other day for a week before giving grit free choice. I have seen situations where it appeared that geese that had been deprived of grit ate such large quantities of sand or pea-size gravel once it was available, that their gizzard became impacted and the birds starved to death because feed could not pass through to the lower intestines.

*Leg Problems

Causes — Probably most leg problems and deformities seen in geese are the result of dietary deficiencies (especially of niacin), a calcium:phosphorus imbalance (common when high calcium laying rations are fed to immature birds), injuries sustained when geese are caught and/or held by their legs, or when birds are run over rough ground or obstacles such as feed troughs. Also important, but normally less common, are inherited leg weaknesses.

Symptoms — Leg problems associated with dietary deficiencies, calcium:phosphorus imbalance or inherited weaknesses are usually signaled by legs that tremble when the goose stands still, give out after the bird walks or runs a relatively short distance, are bowed, or are twisted out at the hock joint. (Also see Spraddled Legs later in this chapter.) Injuries are accompanied by limping, dislocated joints or broken bones.

Treatment — There is no effective treatment for genetic leg weakness or deformities. If otherwise healthy, birds with injured legs will normally recover if kept quiet and provided easy access to food and water. A pond is an excellent place for a goose with a serious leg injury to recover.

When a deficient diet is the cause and prompt action is taken, a vitamin/mineral supplement in the drinking water or mixed with the feed (per manufacturer's recommendation), or the feeding of two to three cups of brewer's dried yeast per ten pounds of feed will often correct the problem. If you have been feeding immature birds a high calcium laying ration, immediately switch to a feed that contains a *maximum* of one percent calcium and a phosphorus:calcium ratio of 1:1 to 1:1.5. (See Phosphorus:Calcium Ratio, Appendix A.)

Prevention — Select breeding birds that have displayed strong limbs from hatching to maturity. Don't catch or carry geese of any age by their legs or run them across rough ground or over equipment such as water and feed troughs. Feed goslings a diet that is fortified with niacin, vitamins D and A, and that has the proper phosphorus to calcium ratio, in the range of 1:1 to 1:1.5 (P:Ca). Young birds should not be fed laying rations since these feeds have too much calcium and an improper phosphorus to calcium ratio which can cause serious problems.

`*Malnutrition

Causes — Malnutrition can be the consequence of either an incomplete diet or an insufficient quantity of feed. It occurs most frequently when geese are raised in buildings or grassless yards and fed nothing but grains or inadequate chicken rations.

Symptoms — In goslings, malnutrition is signaled by stunted growth, wide variation in body size in flocks containing birds of the same age and breed, retarded feather development, weak and/or deformed legs, emaciated birds with little resistance to disease or parasites, and birds that act starved at feeding time. Adult geese that are undernourished produce poorly, often have rough-looking feathers, may be thin and are susceptible to disease and parasites.

Treatment — Provide an ample quantity of food that supplies a balanced diet. (See Nutrition, Chapters 8 and 9.)

Prevention — Geese of any age can starve on a diet of coarse, dry or mature grasses and weeds. Often, people have heard that geese are outstanding grazers, and therefore expect these birds to be able to live on anything that looks like a plant. The only time geese can thrive without being fed grain-based rations is when they have access, throughout most of the day, to succulent and fast-growing grasses. Do not try to save money by starving your birds or using a cheap feed that does not furnish a complete diet. If you feed whole or cracked grains in place of a balanced pelleted ration, make sure the birds have access to grit and a plentiful supply of tender young grass and/or a protein, vitamin and mineral concentrate.

Maggots

Causes & Symptoms — When open wounds are left untreated, especially during warm weather, flies can be attracted which lay eggs on the edges of the sore. In a short time, the eggs hatch into maggots that proceed to feed on the dead tissue of the injury. One of the more common places for waterfowl to harbor maggots is in the area of the vent. Ganders with phallus prostration or geese that develop infections around the vent or have prolapsed oviducts are prime targets. Few sights are more repelling than finding a bird with an open sore that is crawling with maggots. In spite of their gruesome appearance, these grubs do help to clean wounds, but they must be removed before healing can take place.

Treatment — Hold the patient over a hole that has been dug outside of the poultry yard and pour a small amount of turpentine or kerosene into the wound. Repeat as often as necessary to kill all the maggots, and then cover the hole and larva with dirt. To remove the purgative and cleanse the wound, wash the infected area with warm water to which a mild soap has been added, and then rinse thoroughly with clear, warm water. Apply a medicated ointment such as Nitrofurazone, repeating daily until complete healing has taken place.

Prevention — Birds with phallus prostration, prolapsed oviducts or open wounds should be cared for promptly or destroyed.

*Niacin Deficiency

Cause — Goslings are maintained on a diet, such as chick starter, that is deficient in niacin.

Symptoms — Birds develop weak or bowed legs, and often show stunted growth and enlarged hocks. Rickets, sometimes confused with niacin deficiency symptoms, is caused by a vitamin D_3 deficiency or a calcium and/or phosphorus deficiency or imbalance.

Treatment — Goslings exhibiting mild symptoms of a niacin deficiency can often be cured by the immediate addition of a niacin supplement (see Niacin Requirements, Chapter 8) to their feed or drinking water. In severe cases, goslings may become so crippled that they are worthless and must be destroyed.

Prevention — When allowed to graze on tender young grass, goslings seldom are bothered by this malady. However, all goslings, especially those brooded in confinement, should be fed a niacin-rich diet.

*Omphalitis

Causes — When eggs are hatched artificially, the navel of newly hatched birds are sometimes infected by a large variety of bacteria due to poor egg and incubator sanitation. Excessive humidity compounds the problem by slowing down the normal healing process of the navel and providing an ideal habitat for the bacteria.

Symptoms — Trouble is signaled by navels that are large, scabby and inflamed, and abdomens that are abnormally distended and mushy feeling. If not handled and observed closely, goslings with omphalitis can appear fairly normal up until a short time before expiring. Infected birds in advanced stages usually huddle close to the heat source and move about reluctantly. Mortality, which may be light or heavy, invariably takes place between the second and sixth days after hatching.

Treatment — At this time, prevention is the only effective therapy.

Prevention — Omphalitis is rare when sound management is practiced. An adequate number of clean nests that are generously furnished with nesting material is where prevention begins. Soiled hatching eggs should be washed with clean, lukewarm water to which an appropriate sanitizer, such as Germex, has been added. Finally, the incubator and hatcher must be kept clean and should be disinfected after each hatch. Where continuous hatching in the same machine is practiced, fumigation of the incubator is normally required to control omphalitis, particularly in warm, humid climates. Waterfowl eggs should be candled at seven to ten days and again at three weeks to prevent "blowouts" which spew forth millions of virulent bacteria.

Oviduct, Eversion of the

Causes — This ailment seems to be the result of geese straining to lay oversized eggs or from oviduct muscles being weakened due to premature or prolonged egg production or obesity. Inheritance may be a factor since some strains of birds are more susceptible. Unfortunately, this disorder seems to occur most frequently among the best layers.

Symptoms — A goose with this problem is easily identified by her droopy appearance and the expelled oviduct protruding from her vent.

Treatment — An ailing goose can be saved only if she is discovered soon after the oviduct is dislodged and prompt action is taken. Even then, her chances of recovery are marginal.

Before working on the bird, have a helper hold the patient while you wash your hands with hot, soapy water — be sure to clean under your fingernails! To treat, wash the oviduct thoroughly with clean, warm water, then gently push the organ back into place. Confine the goose in a clean pen next to her mate for several days. To give the muscles a chance to heal, the bird should be fed only small quantities of feed, such as greens and whole grains, that will discourage laying.

Geese that are not valuable enough for treatment or whose oviduct is dried, swollen or injured beyond repair, should be killed immediately and disposed of or dressed for meat. Left unattended they will suffer a slow, painful death and the other birds may begin pecking at the dislodged organ.

Prevention — Do not push young geese into laying before they are eight to twelve months old, and make sure females are in good flesh, but not overly fat, at the beginning and throughout the laying season. To keep the oviducts of high-producing females healthy and lubricated, some breeders suggest mixing cod liver oil (one to two teaspoons per bird) with the feed once a week.

*Phallus Prostration

Causes — Under natural conditions, wild ganders normally pair off with a single goose when two or three years old and are sexually active for only a short period each spring. Under domestication, males often breed as yearlings and are mated with two to six geese and are expected to breed over an extended season. A gander will occasionally lose the ability to retract his penis, seemingly caused by unnaturally long and active mating seasons, or possibly a genetic weakness.

Symptoms — The penis, a 1½-inch long (or longer) organ, protrudes from the bird's vent. Frequently, a gander with this disorder will be seen repeatedly shaking his tail from side to side as he attempts to retract the decommissioned organ.

Treatment — Under most circumstances, a gander with this disability should be killed since it is questionable if birds with this weakness should be used for breeding purposes. If the bird is valuable and his problem is discoverd before the penis has become infected or dried out, there is a possibility of recovery. The organ should be washed with clean, warm water and then disinfected and treated with a medicated ointment such as terramycin for mastitis. You can try pushing it back into place, but in my experience — often as not — it will pop back out in a short time. Apply the ointment daily until he is fully recovered, which may require several weeks or longer. Isolating the bird where he has clean, sanitary swimming water seems to facilitate healing.

Prevention — The best safeguard is to have an extra gander so that if one develops this prostration, you'll have a backup male for breeding purposes. It's also a good idea to vent sex all breeding ganders after each breeding season to make sure their penises are still in good working order.

*Poisoning from Medication

Cause — Young geese are frequently poisoned when fed medicated chicken or turkey feeds. In my experience in working with owners of small flocks, medication poisoning is the third leading cause of mortality in young waterfowl, behind losses to drowning and predators. The problem seems to stem from the fact that in proportion to their body weight, geese eat and drink more feed and water than land fowl, getting an overdose of medication. If ingested in the correct dosages, these drugs apparently do not affect geese, young or old, any differently than chickens or turkeys.

Symptoms — Birds (usually goslings that are brooded indoors where they do not have a ready supply of forage to dilute the medication) lose their appetites, become weak, may have stunted growth, show signs of neck paralysis or die suddenly.

Treatment — At the first sign of any of the above symptoms, switch to a non-medicated ration. If medicated feeds must be used, dilute the potency of the drug content by providing an abundant supply of succulent greens and mixing rolled, cracked or small, whole grains with the feed.

Prevention — Unless you have no other choice, do not use medicated rations, particularly if the birds are not able to forage some of their own nourishment. (See Nutrition, Chapter 8 for suggestions of what to feed if you can't purchase non-medicated chick or waterfowl starter rations in your area.)

Poisoning from Plants and Other Substances

Causes — Besides spoiled food (botulism) and certain medications, various other organic and inorganic substances can be poisonous to poultry if ingested in sufficient quantities. Some common materials that are known to be toxic to geese include commercial fertilizers; salt; lead (from birds picking up lead pellets or nibbling on leaded paint); herbicides; pesticides; baits for rats, slugs and snails; plus the seeds of common vetch, cottonseed meal and leaves of tobacco and rhubarb. Other plants that are suspected of causing illness or death in geese include foxglove, potato vines, potatoes that have turned green during the growing season due to exposure to sunlight, and eggplant leaves.

Symptoms — Diagnostic signs vary depending on the poison and the quantity ingested. In general, common symptoms at low or non-fatal levels include retarded growth, droopy appearance and unsteadiness. At high levels, birds may go into convulsions, fling their heads from side to side (apparently attempting to regurgitate the contents of their esophagus) or die suddenly. Due to the free gossypol content of untreated cottonseed meal, excessive feeding (more than 10 to 15 percent of the ration) of this protein supplement can result in suppressed growth, reduced egg production and discolored egg yolks and albumin.

Prevention — Whenever using poisonous baits of any kind, locate them out of the reach of livestock. If commercial fertilizer is applied, do not spill or store it where geese can get to it, and always make certain that the granules are dissolved completely by rain or irrigation before birds are permitted on fertilized pasture. Buildings and equipment with peeling lead base paint must be cleaned up or made inaccessible to geese. Birds should not be allowed to eat sprayed or poisonous plants, salt, or icy slush resulting from snowy driveways or sidewalks being salted in winter. Common vetch seed and cottonseed meal should not be included in a ration for geese at more than 10 to 15 percent. For breeding geese, the use of cottonseed meal is highly questionable.

*Slipped Wing

Causes — A dietary deficiency, extremely fast growth or a genetic defect can all probably cause slipped wings. Some breeders feel this weakness is strictly inherited. However, I find this conclusion difficult to accept since on various occasions I've observed a gaggle of goslings show a high incidence of deformed wings, while other groups, from the same breeding flock and of the same age, but under different management, displayed not a single bird with slipped wings.

Symptoms — The tip of one or both wings folds on the outside of the pinion, rather than resting smoothly against the bird's sides. As the flight feathers of goslings begin to emerge from the wing, it is common for the tip of the wings to project slightly away from the body. However, if the wing is normal, the flight feathers will soon fold under the secondaries. Deformed wings can usually be identified by an obvious gap that develops between the primary and secondary feathers when the wing is opened.

Treatment — When promptly attended, before the bones of the wing harden into position, it is sometimes possible to repair slipped wings of goslings by manually folding the feathered limb in the correct position and binding it shut. Because the wing will become stiff from nonuse, the bandage should be removed after ten to fourteen days, and if need be, retaped after half a day of exercise. On mature birds that cannot be rehabilitated, the visual grotesqueness of projecting wings can be reduced by clipping the flight feathers.

Prevention — The occurrence of slipped wing can be reduced by using only normally winged breeding stock, and by making sure goslings consume a balanced diet. Birds with this deformity are fine for meat or the production of eating eggs.

*Spraddled Legs

Causes — Spraddled legs can usually be traced to smooth bottoms in incubator trays, shipping boxes or brooding floors where goslings have poor footing, but can also be the result of a birth defect.

Symptoms — Goslings are crippled by weak or deformed legs that slide out from under them as they attempt to walk. In acute cases, the legs may protrude at right angles from the body and be totally useless.

Treatment — Birds with severe cases of spraddled legs should be put out of their misery. Mild cases can often be rehabilitated by placing the goslings on a rough surface that gives good footing, such as wood excelsior pads used in chick shipping boxes, coarse burlap or hardware cloth wire. Tying a short piece of yarn between the patient's legs for several days is also helpful in many cases. When hobbles are used, it is essential that they are not tied so tightly that blood circulation is restricted.

Prevention — Slick surfaces on which goslings walk must be covered with a rough material such as wire hardware cloth or burlap for the first week after the birds hatch.

Spraddled legs   Hobbled legs

Staphylococcosis

Causes — The organism, *Staphylococcus aureus*, that causes staph infections can be found in most flocks of poultry, but does not seem to be a serious threat unless geese are in a run-down condition physically due to poor nutrition, parasites, injuries or from being kept in grossly unsanitary quarters.

Symptoms — In the mild form, birds show lameness, an unsteady gait, stand or sit by themselves, move about reluctantly, lose weight and, if not treated promptly, eventually die. In severe cases, the above symptoms can be accompanied by hot, swollen joints, diarrhea and sudden death. Post mortem exams generally show congested and swollen livers, spleens and kidneys.

Treatment — Little is known about treating staph in geese, but the use of gallimycin, terramycin and novobiocin have been suggested.

Prevention — When geese are kept in sanitary conditions and adequately fed, staph is seldom encountered. During rainy weather, the goose yard should not be allowed to deteriorate into filthy, mud-covered cesspools. Birds should not be allowed to walk on sharp objects that may puncture their feet, thus inviting this infection.

*Sticky Eye

Causes — In their natural habitat, geese consume foods high in vitamin A, pantothenic acid and biotin, and have access to clean bathing water. Under domestication, waterfowl are often raised on diets deficient in vitamins and are supplied water in shallow containers which do not permit the birds to rinse their eyes. The result is that geese raised in confinement are susceptible to ophthalmia, a low-grade infection in the eyes which is commonly referred to as sticky eye.

Symptoms — A yellowish discharge mats down the feathers around the eye and may cause the eyelids to stick shut. Sticky eye is most prevalent among goslings that are raised indoors or in filthy conditions outside.

Treatment — As soon as sticky eye is detected, geese should be given a vitamin supplement, fed fresh greens — if possible — and treated with a medicated eye ointment or drops such as Terramycin Eye Drops or Terramycin Ophthalmic Ointment. Providing clean drinking water (to which one drop of Clorox per gallon has been added) in vessels that are sufficiently deep for the birds to submerge their heads and using penicillin tablets or terramycin capsules may speed recovery. If sticky eye is not cured promptly, the infection can linger for the duration of the bird's life and may eventually cause blindness.

Prevention — If goslings are raised in confinement and not fed a ration formulated specifically for waterfowl, fortify their diets with a vitamin premix (such as Vitapol, Headstart or Vitamins & Electrolytes Soluble) or other substances (such as brewer's dried yeast) that are high in vitamin A, biotin and pantothenic acid. Disinfect water fountains weekly with sanitizers such as Germex or Clorox; when feasible, supply water in containers that are sufficiently deep for birds to rinse their eyes. Goslings on pasture seldom have eye problems.

Streptococcosis

Causes & Symptoms — The strep infection found in geese is caused by the bacteria Streptococcus gallinarum and can be introduced into flocks by carrier birds. This disease is uncommon in geese and difficult to diagnose, and is probably occasionally mistaken for fowl cholera due to similar symptoms, including the sudden death of birds that appear to be in good health shortly before expiring. The major organs such as the liver and lungs show congestion and enlargement. Streptococcus must be isolated in the laboratory for positive identification.

Treatment & Prevention — Treatment is difficult since birds often die before infection is suspected. Antibiotics that are useful against gram-positive organisms have been suggested as a prevention, and as a treatment for infected fowl when used at the highest recommended level. Acquiring healthy stock that has been raised in a clean environment and providing sanitary living conditions seem to be the best prevention.

External Parasites

Causes — When waterfowl are raised in clean surroundings, lice and mites seldom multiply on these birds in large enough numbers to be troublesome, especially when bathing water is available. However, goslings that are hatched or brooded by land fowl such as chicken or turkey hens, or adult geese that are kept in filthy surroundings, can harbor harmful infestations of external parasites.

In general, lice are small, flat, yellowish tan insects that normally live their entire life on the host bird. There are a large number of species, but the most common ones found on geese include the wing louse, head and neck louse and body louse. Mites are blood suckers for the most part. Some species, such as the feather mite and depluming mite, stay on the birds most of the time, while the red mite normally is on the birds only while feeding.

Symptoms — The first indication of external parasites can be birds that repeatedly scratch their head and neck with their feet. If you look closely under a good light, body and head and neck lice usually can be seen with the naked eye by parting the feathers of the head, neck and around the vent and oil gland. By holding an open wing up to a light source, such as the sun, wing lice — if present — are visible as dark lines 1/8 to 3/16 inches long in the webbing of the secondary and primary flight feathers. Mites are often overlooked because of their tiny size, plus they often are on the victim at nighttime only. In cases of severe infestations, mites sometimes are visible swarming over the surface of feathers or on the skin when feathers are parted and exposed to sunlight. After handling an infested bird, the miniature ticklike mites may also be seen and felt on your hands and arms.

Lousy geese may have retarded growth, lose weight, lay poorly and be "on edge" from the chewing and scratching of the lice. Mites cause slow growth, anemia, weight loss, deserted nests and even death.

Treatment — Use olive oil, pulverized dried tobacco leaves or a commercial preparation such as Sevin, Malathian or Mange & Lice Control. To be effective, these products need to be worked into the feathers of the head, neck, wings, upper tail, back and vent. When you are dusting or spraying with an insecticide, be extremely careful not to contaminate water or feed with the poison. In case of heavy mite infestations, buildings, nests and roosting areas should be cleaned, disinfected with an approved disinfectant and then sprayed with a product such as Mange & Lice Control.

Prevention — Provide sanitary living conditions. When possible, supply bathing water, especially during warm weather when external parasites are at their worst, or treat birds before lice or mites are present in sufficient numbers to be harmful. Turkey and chicken hens used as foster mothers should always be treated for lice and mites before their maternal chores begin.

Internal Parasites

Causes — Healthy waterfowl consume such copious volumes of water that worms seem to be flushed out of their digestive systems faster than the parasites can reproduce. Worms are normally a problem only when geese have access to stagnant water and crowded ponds or small streams, or when forced to survive in a filthy environment.

A variety of worms occur in poultry.

SPECIES	COLOR	DESCRIPTION	HABITAT
Large round worm	yellowish white	1 to 3 inches long	small intestine
Cecal worm	yellowish white	½ inch long	blind ends of ceca
Capillary worm	whitish	extremely fine, hairlike; up to several inches long	esophagus, upper intestine, or ceca
Gizzard worm	reddish	½ to 1 inch long	under the gizzard lining
Gapeworm	reddish	½ to ¾ inches long; appears Y-shaped when shorter male attaches itself to large female	trachea
Tapeworm	whitish	very short to 6 inches or more; flat, segmented	small intestine

Symptoms — An infestation of worms causes retarded growth, lowered feed conversion and reduced egg production. (In the case of gapeworms, birds often can be seen and heard attempting to clear their windpipe by shaking their head vigorously and coughing.) In severe cases, the above symptoms are accompanied by weight loss, weakness, diarrhea, and, if not treated promptly, eventually death. Upon post mortem examination, most species of worms can be found in their appropriate habitat, if they are present in significant numbers.

Treatment — Poultry worm medications that are added to the drinking water are readily available and easy to use. Some wormers are prepared for only one species of parasite, while others have a combination of ingredients and are effective against a number of worm species. Check with your feed or poultry supply dealer for brands that are available and then follow the instructions carefully. In the case of a continuing worm problem, a carefully planned worming schedule as outlined by the manufacturer will need to be employed to eradicate the parasites. De-worming geese that are laying can negatively effect egg production and hatchability. Some people have suggested diatomaceous earth or a pinch or two of chewing tobacco pushed down each bird's gullet as alternative remedies.

Prevention — Provide fresh drinking water and sanitary living quarters. Most worms cannot survive in a dry, clean environment, so keep bedding dry, well-stirred and deep enough to absorb the droppings. Watering vessels should always be placed on wire or slat covered platforms. In localities where worms are a major problem, birds should be routinely wormed according to the manufacturer's recommendations.

PRECAUTIONS WHEN USING DRUGS AND PESTICIDES

When used according to the instructions and in conjunction with good management practices, the occasional use of drugs and pesticides can be useful in maintaining the health and productivity of poultry flocks. However, if over or misused, these aids can be detrimental and pose health hazards to both animals and humans. Always follow directions carefully and use only the dosages that are recommended for the specific problem at hand. Don't fall into the trap of thinking that if one dose is good, then a double dose must be better. To keep from poisoning you and your family or customers with potentially dangerous drugs, be sure to follow recommended withdrawal periods when treating meat or egg producing birds. And last but not least, store all drugs and pesticides in their original containers in a dry, clean location out of the reach of children and animals.

PULLORUM-TYPHOID BLOOD TESTING

Pullorum and Fowl Typhoid are two types of highly contagious Salmonella infections that can be passed from breeding stock to their offspring through hatching eggs or by infected birds coming in contact with healthy birds. Since these diseases are easily transported from one locality to another, some states — and most countries — require that all adult poultry crossing their borders, either for breeding stock or for exhibiting in a show, must be blood tested for pullorum-typhoid and certified clean prior to their entrance. In the case of transporting or shipping day-old poultry, the parent stock must be certified clean.

For the small flock owner, blood testing is not usually required (although it's not a bad idea and is relatively inexpensive in states that cooperate with the National Poultry Improvement Plan) except if birds are to be exhibited or sold in states requiring a health permit. If you acquire your stock from breeders who do not annually blood test their birds, there is some risk of an outbreak occurring.

For waterfowl and chickens, the pullorum-typhoid test is normally performed by extracting a small amount of blood from under the bird's wing and mixing it with a drop of antigen on a light table. If the test results are negative (indicating that the bird is not a carrier), the blood and antigen remain blended, while positive results (signifying that the bird may be an infected carrier) are signaled by pronounced coagulation or curdling shortly after the blood and antigen are combined. To be validated, blood tests must be performed by a licensed technician. For more information, contact the veterinary office of your state or province Department of Agriculture.

POST MORTEM EXAMINATION

Most of us who raise poultry have experienced the disappointment of finding an expired bird that was in good flesh and showed no outward signs of disease or attack from a predator. When this situation occurs, there are three basic options of what to do: 1) dispose of the carcass and never know what caused the bird's demise, 2) take the fowl to a diagnostic laboratory or veterinarian for diagnosis, or 3) perform a post mortem yourself and see if the problem can be located.

The first of the three choices is probably the most common but definitely the least desirable. The second is most desirable but least common and sometimes impractical, except when a serious or contagious disease is suspected. While most lay persons cannot expect to approach the proficiency of trained diagnostic specialists, the third alternative can be useful in identifying many problems, thus averting further mortality or lowered production due to treatable ailments.

Equipment Needed

The average household contains the few tools needed to perform a basic post mortem examination. A small, sharp knife (which afterwards should not be used on human food) is needed for cutting open the bird. A pair of scissors is useful for incising the trachea (windpipe), esophagus, intestines and ceca. A magnifying glass is helpful in searching for internal parasites such as hard-to-see capillary and cecal worms. The work bench should be covered with newspapers and located in a well-lit area. CAUTION: After a post mortem, all tools must be sterilized and the work area disinfected to guard against spreading infections and disease to humans and livestock.

Major Diagnostic Organs

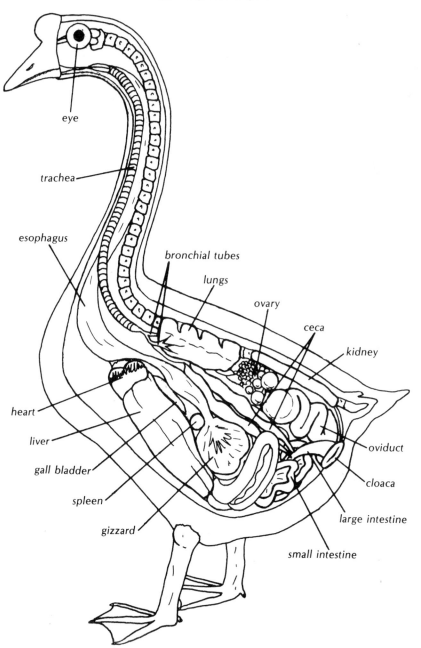

Post Mortem Examination (with breast removed)

1 throat
2 esophagus
3 trachea (windpipe)
4 heart
5 lungs
6 liver
7 gizzard
8 small intestine
9 large intestine
10 vent

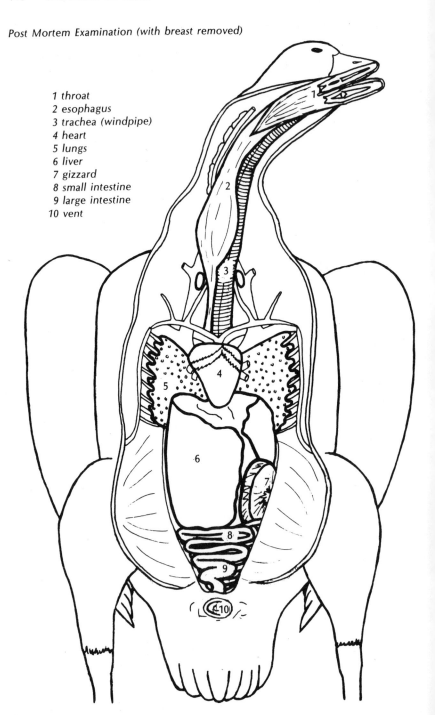

Procedure for a Basic Post Mortem

When examining waterfowl, I have adapted the following procedure, although the sequence of the examination varies according to the circumstances. If an esophagus or gizzard impaction is suspected, these organs are inspected first, while if worms are a prime candidate, then the intestines are examined, etc.

1. Cut and spread open the bird from one corner of the mouth to the vent.
2. Scan the body cavity and organs for hemorrhages and tumors.
3. In mature females, examine the body cavity and oviduct for abnormalities such as internally laid eggs, blocked oviduct or obesity.
4. Examine the liver for discoloration, tiny light spots, light streaks, dark hemorrhagic areas, hardness or yellow coating of waxy substance.
5. Cut open the gizzard and check for hard mass of string or other material, eroded inner lining or serious damage. Peel off the horny inner lining and look for uncharacteristic bumps which may indicate gizzard worms.
6. Open the esophagus and look for blockage or injury.
7. Examine the main organs (liver, heart, spleen, lungs, kidneys and ovaries) for obvious deformities and discoloration.
8. Slit open the small and large intestines and ceca, checking for worms, blood, inflamed linings, hemorrhages and yellow cheesy nodules.
9. Split the trachea lengthwise and inspect for blockage, gapeworms, blood, excess mucous and cheesy material.
10. When finished with the examination, clean up and dispose of the carcass and all debris, disinfect the tools and thoroughly wash your hands and arms with soap and warm water.

CHAPTER 12

Butchering

The raising and preparation of homegrown foods is a wholesome activity. While the actual slaughtering of animals is an unpleasant task, for those of us who are not vegetarians, butchering our own meat helps remind us that a life has been sacrificed whenever we partake of animal flesh.

Because fresh meats are highly susceptible to contamination and spoilage, cleanliness throughout the butchering process is essential. All cutting utensils that will be used should be sharpened ahead of time since dull axes, knives and cleavers waste time and are unsafe.

WHEN TO BUTCHER

The most time-consuming chore in butchering waterfowl is the removal of their feathers. To make plucking as simple as possible, geese must be slaughtered when they are in full feather. The day before butchering I like to catch several of the birds, parting the plumage with my fingers at two or three locations both on the back and breast to check for pin feathers. If a goose is dressed when covered with pin feathers, a picking job that normally should take no more than ten to twenty minutes can drag on much longer.

Depending on breed, strain and management, goslings normally are in full feather briefly sometime between the ages of nine to twelve weeks. Shortly after acquiring their first set of feathers, young geese go into a heavy molt, replacing their juvenile garb with adult plumage. If goslings are not dressed before this molt commences, it's best to delay butchering for six to ten weeks when they should be in full feather once again, or the birds can be skinned rather than plucked. Geese are not considered to be in prime flesh while they are molting.

PREKILLING PREPARATIONS

Geese should be taken off feed four to six hours prior to killing or the night before, if they are going to be dressed early the following morning, so their esophagus and intestines will be empty when drawn. To avoid excessive shrinkage, drinking water should be left in front of the birds until an hour or so before they are slaughtered.

KILLING

There are several ways of dispatching geese. The simplest and most impersonal method is the ax and chopping block. To hold the bird's head securely in place, it is helpful to have a device such as two large nails driven into the block to form a V. The necks of geese are thick and tough, so a sharp cutting edge on the ax is a must. As soon as the head is removed, the bird should be hung by its legs to promote thorough bleeding and to prevent it from becoming bruised or soiled from thrashing about on the ground. Since large geese can be difficult to restrain, before killing them it is helpful to securely tie their legs together. Then place them headfirst into a turkey-size metal killing cone or a burlap bag. If a bag is used, tie the top of it shut and pull the bird's head and neck through a hole that has been cut out of one bottom corner. After the ax has fallen, the bird can be hung in the cone or bag for bleeding.

A second method for killing is to suspend the live goose head down with leg shackles (which can be made from heavy gauge, smooth wire) or in a killing cone or sack as described above. Firmly grasping the bill with one hand, stun

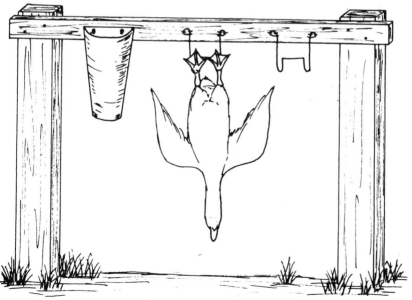

Killing cone and leg shackles

the bird by hitting it sharply at the base of the skull with a stout stick. Then using a sharp knife, cut the throat on one or both sides about one inch below and parallel to the jawbone, severing the jugular vein and carotid artery. The cut must be made sufficiently deep to allow free bleeding. The head should remain intact, providing a convenient handle if the bird is scalded.

To avoid discolored meat in the dressed product, it is vital that geese are bled thoroughly before they are processed further.

PICKING

The sooner a goose is picked after it is bled, the easier the feathers can be extracted. Some literature claims that most of a day is required to pluck a goose. However, if after some experience, it takes you more than a half hour per bird, then there's a mighty good chance that you are butchering at the wrong time or that your technique could be improved.

Dry Picking

It has been said that the best quality feathers for filler material and the most attractive carcasses are obtained when geese are dry picked. However, there is little — if any — difference in the quality between wet and dry picked feathers, if the former are handled properly. Most people, including myself, find dry picking unbearably slow. One secret for success is to extract feathers in the same direction they grow. Pulling feathers against the grain invariably results in torn skin. For a better grip the bird can be lightly dusted with resin, or your hands periodically moistened with water. The larger plumes of the wings and tail need to be plucked out one or two at a time.

Because feathers and down float in every direction when waterfowl are dry picked, it is wise to carefully choose a setting that is free of drafts. Picking into large plastic garbage bags and covering the floor around the plucking area with newspapers are helpful in keeping feathers under control.

Scald Picking

The most common method for defeathering geese is to scald them prior to picking. The equipment needed for this procedure includes a stove, hotplate or fire for heating water and one or two heat resistant containers that are sufficiently large to completely submerge an entire goose. You may also want to rig up a scalding stick (see illustration) which is useful in keeping the bird submerged while scalding.

To scald, hold the goose by its feet and attach the scalding stick to the bird's neck. Then, vigorously dip the carcass up and down in water that is 145° to 155° F (63° to 68° C), making certain that the water penetrates through to the skin. To improve the wetting ability of the scalding water, a small amount of

Scalding stick

detergent can be added. I like to use a double-dunk method, utilizing soapy water for the first minute or so, then finishing the job with clear, scalding water. This second dipping removes the slippery film of the detergent, giving a better grip on feathers.

The scalding time for geese varies from 1½ to 3 minutes or longer, depending on water temperature, age of the bird and time of year. Mature geese, particularly after cold weather has set in, require longer and hotter scalds than young birds. Since geese have such a thick covering of feathers and down on their sides and underbody, I have found it helpful to scald the entire bird for 1½ to 2 minutes, and then scald the breast an additional minute by pulling the carcass back and forth across the top of the water. When properly scalded, one should be able to rough pick a goose — remove 90 percent of all feathers and down — in less than five minutes. If you find that the feathers are still difficult to remove after the initial scald, the bird can be redipped. However, overscalding should be avoided since it causes the skin to tear easily and discolors the carcass with dark blotches.

Geese should be picked immediately after scalding. The wing and tail plumes should be removed first and kept separate if the down and small feathers are going to be saved for filler. Because the feathers are hot after scalding, have a bucket of cold water nearby in which to dip your hands. Hard-to-get pin feathers and small tufts of down can be gripped between your thumb and the blade of a knife.

If your first attempts at scald picking do not produce carcasses that are as attractive as those that are processed commercially, don't get discouraged. Your results should improve once you've gained some experience. Feathers from scalded geese are of good quality and valuable when handled correctly (see Care of Feathers at the end of this chapter).

Wax Picking

A popular and recommended variation of the scalding method is to dip geese in hot wax after they have been scalded and partially defeathered. When done properly, wax can produce clean carcasses in a short time, even when birds with a moderate number of pin feathers are butchered. While there are products such as Dux-Wax, which are manufactured specifically for this purpose and are available from poultry supply distributors (see Appendix I), straight paraffin or a mixture of one part beeswax to one part paraffin usually works satisfactorily.

Extreme caution must always be taken when working with hot wax since this substance is highly combustible and if splashed onto your skin can cause painful and deep burns. Wax must never come into contact with open flames or heating elements, nor should it be heated directly on the burner of a stove or hotplate. It is safest to melt wax in a double boiler or when floating on top of water.

There are several methods which can be used for preparing wax to be used in dressing waterfowl. One of the most satisfactory systems for home dressing is to use a hotplate and a metal container — such as a large old kettle or bucket —

that's sufficiently spacious to hold a goose. (I like to use a five-gallon bucket that is three-quarters full of water.) Then, sufficient wax is added to cover the water's surface with a one- to two-inch layer of melted wax. Some commercial processors recommend holding the wax at a temperature of 150° to 170° F (66° to 77° C), but I prefer to have the liquid gently bubbling — approximately 200° F (93° C) — although a full rolling boil is too hot.

When the wax is ready, the rough picked bird is submerged into the hot liquid several times. Immerse the carcass in cold water or wait long enough between each dunking to allow congealing to build up a good layer of wax. To encourage the wax to cling to the feathers, it is sometimes helpful to partially dry the goose prior to waxing, although when the hotter wax (200° F or 93° C) is used, drying usually is unnecessary. If only a few birds are being dressed, you may find it simpler to melt a small amount of wax which is then poured over the carcass.

Submerging the waxed goose in cold water causes the wax to harden and grip the feathers. The wax and feathers are then stripped off together, resulting in a finished product that is clean and attractive. Birds that are extra pinny can be rewaxed. Used wax can be recycled by boiling it and straining out the down, pins and feathers.

SINGEING

Long hairlike filament feathers remain after geese are dry or scald picked. The simplest way to remove these filoplumes is to quickly pass the carcass over a flame, being careful not to burn or blacken the skin with smoke. A jar lid with a thin layer of rubbing alcohol covering the bottom gives the best flame I know for singeing. Alcohol burns tall, cleanly and odor-free. Newspapers (do not use colored sheets) loosely rolled into a hand torch, gas burners and candles can also be used, although they have a tendency to blacken the skin and impart a disagreeable flavor if one is not careful.

SKINNING

Geese can be skinned rather than picked. Some advantages of this technique are that birds with pin feathers can be dressed as easily as those in full feather and some people find skinning less time-consuming than picking. Because skin is composed mostly of fat, skinning also reduces the fat content of the dressed goose. The major drawbacks of this method are that skinned carcasses lose much of their eye appeal when roasted whole, some flavor is lost, a higher percentage of the bird is wasted and special precautions must be taken in cooking the meat to prevent dryness.

To prepare a goose for skinning, remove its head, tail, feet and the last joint of each wing. With the bird resting on its back, slip the blade of a small, sharp knife under the skin of the neck, and slit the skin the length of the body along the keel bone, cutting around both sides of the vent. The final step is to peel the skin off, which requires a good deal of pulling. Over stubborn areas, such as the back, a knife may be needed to trim the skin loose.

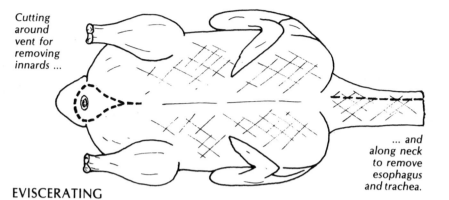

Cutting around vent for removing innards ...

... and along neck to remove esophagus and trachea.

EVISCERATING

Geese can be drawn immediately after they have been defeathered, or they can be chilled in ice water for several hours or hung in a cool (33° to 36° F, .6° to 2° C) location to ripen for six to twenty-four hours. Chilling the carcasses first has the advantage of making the cleaning procedure less messy, while aging before eviscerating produces stronger flavored meat, which is preferred by some people.

With the bird resting on a clean, smooth surface (we use our dishrack drainboard), remove the feet, head and oil gland, making certain that both yellowish lobes of the oil gland are cut out. Then make a shallow three- to four-inch long horizontal incision between the end of the breastbone and the vent, being careful not to puncture the intestines that lie just under the skin. Through this incision insert your hand into the body cavity and gently loosen the organs from the inside walls of the body and pull them out. Cut around the vent to disconnect the intestines from the carcass. The gizzard, heart and liver should be cut free and set aside before the unwanted innards are discarded.

The esophagus (geese do not have true crops) and windpipe are well-anchored in the neck and require a vigorous pull to remove them. The pink, spongy lungs are located against the back among the ribs and can be scraped out with the fingers if you desire.

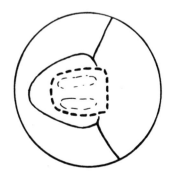

Cutting out oil gland on top side of tail

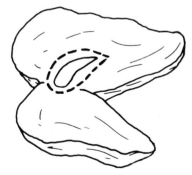

Incision to remove green gall bladder from liver

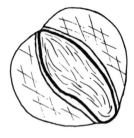
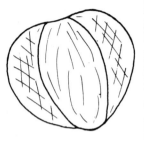

Cutting open gizzard   Taking out contents   Cleaned gizzard

To clean gizzards, cut around their outside edge — preferably without severing the inner bag — and then pull the two halves apart. The inner bag with its contents of feed and grit can then be peeled away and discarded. The final step is to rinse the muscular organ with water.

The gall bladder, a small greenish sac, is tightly anchored to the liver and should be removed intact since it is filled with bitter-tasting bile. A portion of the liver should be cut off along with the gall bladder so bile does not spill onto edible meat.

Unwanted feathers and body parts make excellent fertilizer and should be buried near a tree or in the garden sufficiently deep to prevent scavengers from unearthing them. Raw innards should not be put on the compost heap or fed raw to cats and dogs. If you give uncooked entrails to your pets, they can develop a taste for poultry and may start killing birds to satisfy their cravings. However, cooked offal is an excellent protein supplement to the diet of hogs or meat-eating pets.

COOLING THE MEAT

After all the organs have been removed, thoroughly wash the carcass and chill to a temperature of 34° to 40° F (1° to 4° C) as soon as possible. If meat is cooled too slowly, bacteria may grow, causing spoilage and unpleasant flavor. Poultry can be chilled in ice water or air cooled by hanging the carcasses in a refrigerator or in a room with a temperature of 30° to 40° F (-1° to 4° C). When air cooled, waterfowl that have been scalded or wax picked should be placed in plastic bags to prevent their skin from drying out and discoloring.

PACKAGING AND STORING MEAT

After the body heat has dissipated from the carcasses, they should be sealed in airtight containers. If the meat was chilled in water, it should be allowed to drain for five to ten minutes before being packaged. To retain the highest quality in meat that is going to be frozen, the air can be sucked from plastic bags with a straw or vacuum cleaner before sealing. If shrinkable bags are used (and they are recommended), after the air has been removed, the packaged bird should be submerged in boiling water for several seconds or have boiling water poured over it from a teapot. To produce the tenderest meat, it is generally considered necessary to age poultry twelve to thirty-six hours at 33° to 40° F (.6° to 4° C) before it is eaten or frozen.

CARE OF FEATHERS

Goose feathers are a valuable byproduct of butchering. If you plan to save the feathers, keep the down and small body feathers separate from the large stiff plumes of the wings, tail and body as the slaughtered birds are being picked.

When geese are scalded prior to picking, the feathers should be washed with a gentle detergent and rinsed thoroughly in warm water. (If a washer and dryer are available, feathers can be placed in a pillowcase and washed and dried in this manner.) Spread feathers out several inches thick on a clean, dry surface or place loosely in cloth sacks of porous fabric — such as burlap or cheese cloth — and hang in a warm room or on the clothesline. Wet feathers should be fluffed and stirred several times daily. Once they are well dried, feathers can be bagged and stored in a clean, dry location. (See Appendix E for instructions on how to use feathers.)

BUTCHERING CHECK LIST

1. Remove the birds' feed four to six hours before they are killed.
2. Sharpen all cutting tools that will be used for butchering.
3. When catching geese prior to butchering, keep them calm and handle carefully to avoid discolored meat due to bruises.
4. Hang slaughtered geese in killing cones or by their feet to avoid bruising or soiling the meat and to insure thorough bleeding.
5. Remove feathers as soon as possible after birds are bled.
6. Singe off filament feathers.
7. Trim out the oil gland from the base of the tail.
8. Cut off feet and shanks at hock joints; remove head.
9. Make a horizontal incision between the vent and the end of the breast-bone, and gently lift out the innards.
10. Set aside the heart, gizzard and liver before disposing of unwanted viscera.
11. Pull out the windpipe and esophagus from the neck/chest area.
12. Extract the lungs from between the ribs (optional).
13. Rinse the carcass thoroughly with clean, cold water.
14. Clean gizzard and carefully remove gall bladder from the liver.
15. Chill dressed birds to an internal temperature of 40° F (4° C) or less.
16. Bury unwanted body parts, entrails and feathers or cook for pet food.
17. Age the meat for twelve to thirty-six hours at 33° to 40° F (.6° to 4° C) prior to cooking or freezing.
18. Package and freeze the meat, or enjoy a festive banquet.

Appendices

APPENDIX A

Formulating Goose Rations

There are situations when it is advantageous to be able to formulate feeds that utilize readily available local ingredients. With the aid of a hand calculator and by carefully following the information in this appendix, you should be able to create nutritionally sound goose rations that fit your specific needs. Whenever possible, it is a good idea to have a poultry nutritionist (contact your local agriculture extension specialist) check over your formula for obvious inadequacies.

The purpose of this section is to present the basic nutrient requirements of geese and summarize the fundamental procedures for formulating rations. If you are interested in the whys of nutrition, see Appendix J for sources of information.

USING THE FORMULA CHART

The formula chart (see Table 22) is a convenient and orderly means by which rations can be computed. Ingredients and their values for protein, energy, fiber, etc., are taken from Table 21 (or similar chart) and written or typed into the proper columns of the formula chart. The percentage (which should be expressed as a decimal, e.g., 73 percent wheat ÷ 100 = .73) at which each ingredient is going to be included in a ration is then multiplied times the various nutrients of the ingredient.

Once the protein values have been calculated for each ingredient, they should be added up to see if the protein content of the ration compares favorably with the recommendations given in Table 20. Once the proper protein content has been obtained, the values for energy, fat, fiber, minerals, vitamins and amino acids should be computed and compared with Table 20.

CONVERTING KILOGRAMS TO POUNDS

In many publications containing information showing the average composition of feedstuff for poultry (similar to Table 21), the values for the various nutrients are given in kilograms. If you'd rather work in the American Standard rather than the Metric system of weights and measures, a conversion must be made. One kilogram equals 2.2 pounds so to convert kilograms to pounds, divide by 2.2. Example: Wheat has approximately 3,120 kcal/kg of metabolizable energy, which if divided by 2.2, gives 1418 kcal/lb of ME. (If you want to work in the Metric system, the values in Tables 20 and 21 must be converted from pounds to kilograms by multiplying by 2.2). Those values that are given in percentages (such as protein, calcium, phosphorus, etc.) remain the same no matter which system is used.

COMPUTING THE CALORIE:PROTEIN RATIO

Birds eat primarily to meet their energy needs. To guard against over- or under-consumption of protein by geese, rations must have the proper calorie to protein ratio (see Table 20). To compute this ratio, divide the metabolizable energy (kcal per pound of feed) by the protein percentage of the ration (e.g., 1278 kcal of energy ÷ 15.8 percent protein is equal to a calorie to protein ration of 1:81 or simply 81.

THE PHOSPHORUS:CALCIUM RATIO

In order for geese (particularly young ones) to utilize phosphorus and calcium effectively, these two minerals must be included in feeds in the proper proportions. An imbalance of the phosphorus and calcium can result in stunted growth, rickets and other bone deformities, and in acute cases, lead to death.

For goslings and non-producing adults, the correct ratio of total phosphorus to calcium is in the range of 1:1 to 1:1.5 (P:Ca), with 1:1.2 considered ideal. For laying birds, the ratio should fall between 1:3.5 and 1:4.25.

To compute the phosphorus:calcium ratio of a ration, divide the amount of calcium by the quantity of total phosphorus. Example: A starting ration contains .80 percent calcium and .65 percent total phosphorus (.80 ÷ .65 = 1.2 which is equal to a P:Ca ratio of 1:1.2).

USING A PROTEIN CONCENTRATE

In many instances, the simplest method for preparing a balanced and economical ration at home is by mixing a commercial protein concentrate with locally grown grains. If fortified with additional niacin, concentrates formulated for chickens normally work satisfactorily for geese as well.

To calculate the proportions of concentrate to grains that should be used, the Pearson's Square Method can be employed. Example: You have a concentrate that is 40 percent protein and want to blend it with soft wheat (approximately 10 percent protein) to get a 20 percent protein breeder ration.

To obtain the correct proportions of wheat and concentrate, subtract the smaller number from the larger on each diagonal (i.e., 20 - 10 = 10 parts concentrate and 40 - 20 = 20 parts wheat). Then divide the parts of each by the total number of parts and multiply by 100 to get the percentage at which each ingredient should be used.

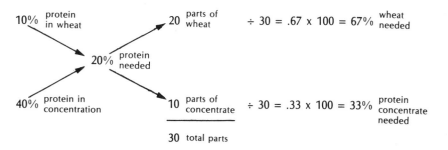

10% protein in wheat   20 parts of wheat   ÷ 30 = .67 x 100 = 67% wheat needed

20% protein needed

40% protein in concentration   10 parts of concentrate   ÷ 30 = .33 x 100 = 33% protein concentrate needed

30 total parts

TABLE 20   RECOMMENDED NUTRIENT LEVELS FOR COMPLETE GOOSE
RATIONS (Pelleted)[1]
(Expressed as a percentage or amount per pound of feed)

Nutrient	Starter 0-4 Wks.	Grower 5-8 Wks.	Grower-Finisher	Breeder Layer	Holding Ration
*Metabolizable energy (kcal/lb)[2]	1350 ± 25	1350 ± 25	1350 ± 25	1250 ± 25	1200 ± 25
*Energy:Protein ratio	68	84	84	78	100
*Fat, minimum (%)	3.0	2.5	2.0	2.0	1.5
*Fiber, maximum (%)	4.0	5	6	6	7
*Protein, minimum (%)	20[3]	16[3]	16	16[3]	12
Amino Acids, minimum:					
Arginine (%)	1.25	1.00	1.00	.95	.83
Glycine + serine (%)	1.12	.90	.90	.85	.74
Histidine (%)	.44	.35	.35	.30	.26
Isoleucine (%)	.88	.70	.70	.65	.57
Leucine (%)	1.63	1.30	1.30	1.20	1.05
*Lysine (%)	.94	.75	.75	.70	.62
*Methionine + cystine (%)	.75	.60	.60	.55	.48
*Methionine (%)	.44	.35	.35	.30	.26
Phenylalanine + tyrosine (%)	1.63	1.30	1.30	1.20	1.05
Phenylalanine (%)	.88	.70	.70	.65	.57
Threonine (%)	.75	.60	.60	.55	.48
Tryptophan (%)	.24	.19	.19	.17	.15
Valine (%)	1.00	.80	.80	.75	.66
Vitamins (fat soluble), (Amount to be added):					
*Vitamin A (IU)	4500	3250	3250	4500	3250
*Vitamin D3 (ICU)	600	500	500	800	500
*Vitamin E (IU)	6.0	5.0	5.0	7.5	5.0
*Vitamin K (mg)	1.0	1.0	.5	1.0	.5
Vitamins (water soluble), (Total amount in ration):					
Thiamine (mg)	1.25	1.25	1.25	1.25	1.25
*Riboflavin (mg)	3.75	2.25	2.25	3.75	2.25
*Pantothenic acid (mg)	7	6	5	7	5
*Niacin, available (mg)[4]	35	30	25	35	25
Pyridoxine (mg)	1.50	1.50	1.50	1.75	1.50
Biotin (mg)	.10	.07	.07	.10	.07
*Choline (mg)	800	700	500	650	500
Folacin (mg)	.35	.20	.20	.35	.20
*Vitamin B12 (mg)	.006	.005	.004	.006	.004
Linoleic acid (%)[5]	1.0	.8	.8	1.0	.8
Minerals:					
*Calcium, minimum (%)	.7	.6	.6	2.25	.6
maximum (%)	1.0	1.0	1.0	2.75	1.0
Phosphorus, total (minimum %)	.65	.60	.60	.65	.60
*Phosphorus, available minimum (%)	.40	.35	.35	.40	.35
maximum (%)	.60	.55	.55	.60	.55
Potassium (%)	.4	.4	.3	.2	.2
*Sodium (%)[6]	.18-.22	.18-.22	.18-.22	.18-.22	.18-.22
Chloride (%)[6]	.12	.12	.12	.12	.12
Copper (mg)	2.0	1.5	1.5	2.0	1.5
Iodine (mg)	.2	.2	.2	.2	.2
Iron (mg)	40	20	20	30	20
Magnesium (mg)	300	275	275	300	275
*Manganese (mg)	25	25	25	20	20
Selenium (mg)[7]	.08	.08	.08	.08	.08
*Zinc (mg)	18	18	18	30	18

TABLE 20- continued

[1]Because birds eat primarily to satisfy their energy requirements, keep in mind that the nutrient levels shown in this table apply only to the energy level specified. For rations containing different energy concentrations, compensations in the quantities of amino acids, vitamins and minerals should be made to guard against over- or under-consumption of these nutrients. If your ration has a lower energy level than given in this table, the amount of the other nutrients can likewise be reduced to avoid waste. Example: Your starter ration has an energy level of 1250 kcal/lb, which is 93% of 1350 kcal/lb (1250 ÷ 1350 = .926 x 100 = 93%). Therefore, all nutrients can be reduced by approximately 7% and the birds will still ingest the proper quantities of all nutrients, since they will consume approximately 7% more of the 1250 kcal/lb feed than they would of the 1350 kcal/lb ration.

[2]The energy concentration given is only an example. Provided the concentration of each nutrient per unit of energy remains the same, the energy concentration of rations may vary from 1000 to 1500 kcal/lb, except for breeding rations which probably should be kept close to the range of 1200 to 1300 kcal/lb. The energy level chosen should be the one at which least cost per unit of energy is achieved.

[3]Some breeders feel goslings grow faster and adult geese reproduce better if these protein levels are increased by 2 to 4%.

[4]Most of the niacin in plants is unavailable to birds.

[5]Rations based on wheat, milo or barley are often deficient in linoleic acid, necessitating the addition of an ingredient rich in this fatty acid, such as one of the vegetable oils.

[6]These recommendations are for birds receiving low salt drinking water. The salt content of rations should be reduced if drinking water contains above average levels of sodium chloride.

[7]Grains grown in areas where the soil is of volcanic origin often are deficient in selenium.

*An asterisk denotes the nutrients that are of greatest concern when formulating rations. Usually, if these are balanced, the others will be satisfactory.

Note: Some information from this table was adapted from *Nutrient Requirements of Poultry* 7th revised ed. (1977), pages 30 and 33, with the permission of the National Academy of Sciences, Washington, D.C.

Key: IU = International Units
      ICU = International Chick Units
      mg = milligram
      kcal = kilocalories

TABLE 21 AVERAGE COMPOSITION OF SOME COMMONLY USED FEEDS FOR POULTRY

Line No.	Feedstuff	Protein %	Energy kcal/lb	Crude Fat %	Crude Fiber %	Calcium %	Total Phosphorus %	Avail. Phosphorus %	Sodium %	Manganese mg/lb
	Alfalfa meal, dehydrated									
1	17% Protein	17.5	622.73	2.0	24.1	1.44	0.22	0.22	0.12	13.6
2	20% Protein	20.0	740.91	3.6	20.2	1.67	0.28	0.28	0.13	19.2
3	Barley	11.6	1200.00	1.8	5.1	0.03	0.36	0.11	0.04	—
4	Barley, Pacific Coast	9.0	1190.91	2.0	6.4	0.05	0.32	0.10	0.02	7.4
5	Corn, yellow	8.8	1559.09	3.8	2.2	0.02	0.28	0.08	0.02	2.3
6	Corn, Gluten meal, 41%	41.0	1336.36	2.5	7.0	0.23	0.55	0.16	0.07	4.0
7	Dicalcium phosphate	—	—	—	—	21.00	18.50	18.50	1.20	54.5
8	Distiller's dried solubles (corn)	28.5	1331.82	9.0	4.0	0.35	1.33	0.39	0.26	33.5
9	DL-Methionine, 98%	—	—	—	—	—	—	—	—	—
10	Fish meal, herring	72.3	1450.00	10.0	0.7	2.29	1.70	1.70	0.61	2.1
11	Fish meal, menhaden	60.5	1281.82	9.4	0.7	5.11	2.88	2.88	0.41	15.0
12	Limestone, ground	—	—	—	—	38.00	—	—	0.06	112.5
13	Meat and bone meal	50.4	890.91	8.6	2.8	10.10	4.96	4.96	0.72	6.4
14	Meat meal	54.4	909.09	7.1	8.7	8.27	4.10	4.10	1.15	4.4
15	Oats	11.4	1159.09	4.2	10.8	0.06	0.27	0.08	0.08	19.6
16	Oats, West Coast	9.0	1186.36	—	11.0	0.08	0.30	0.09	—	17.3
17	Oyster shell	0.9	18.18	—	—	37.26	0.07	0.07	0.20	58.0
18	Salt, iodized	—	—	—	—	—	—	—	38.91	—
19	Sorghum, grain (milo)	8.9	1531.82	2.8	2.3	0.03	0.28	0.09	0.04	6.2
20	Soybean meal, solvent 50%	50.8	1131.36	1.1	2.9	0.29	0.65	0.20	0.01	20.9
21	Soybean meal, solvent 44%	44.0	1013.64	0.8	7.3	0.29	0.65	0.20	0.26	13.3
22	Soybean meal, dehulled	48.5	1109.09	1.0	3.9	0.27	0.62	0.19	0.25	19.5
23	Wheat, bran	15.7	590.91	3.0	11.0	0.14	1.15	0.35	0.05	51.5
24	Wheat, hard	14.1	1272.73	1.9	2.4	0.05	0.37	0.11	0.04	14.5
25	Wheat, middlings	16.0	818.18	3.0	7.5	0.12	0.90	0.28	0.12	53.6
26	Wheat, soft	10.2	1418.18	1.8	2.4	0.05	0.31	0.10	0.04	10.8
27	Whey, dried	12.0	863.64	0.8	0.2	0.97	0.76	0.76	0.48	2.8
28	Yeast, brewer's, dried	44.4	904.55	1.0	2.7	0.12	1.40	0.41	0.07	2.4

TABLE 21- continued

Line No.	Zinc mg/lb	Vit. A IU/lb	Vit. E mg/lb	Vit. K mg/lb	Ribo-flavin mg/lb	Panto-thenic Acid mg/lb	Total Niacin mg/lb	Choline mg/lb	Vit. B$_{12}$ mg/lb	Ly-sine %	Methi-onine %	Cys-tine %
1	10.9	83,909	56.82	4.0	6.2	11.4	17.3	637	.0018	0.73	0.23	0.20
2	11.4	101,000	65.46	4.7	6.9	15.5	18.2	645	.0018	0.87	0.31	0.25
3	7.7	—	9.09	—	0.8	3.6	25.0	450	—	0.40	0.17	0.19
4	6.8	—	9.09	—	0.7	3.2	21.8	470	—	0.29	0.13	0.18
5	4.5	1318	10.00	—	0.5	1.8	10.9	282	—	0.24	0.20	0.15
6	9.1	11,955	9.09	—	0.8	4.5	22.7	421	—	0.78	1.03	0.65
7	13.6	—	—	—	—	—	—	—	—	—	—	—
8	38.6	500	18.18	—	7.7	9.5	52.7	2201	—	0.90	0.50	0.40
9	—	—	—	—	—	—	—	—	—	—	98.00	—
10	60.0	—	10.00	—	4.5	7.7	42.3	2412	.1832	5.70	2.10	0.72
11	66.8	—	3.18	—	2.2	4.1	25.0	1389	.0473	4.83	1.78	0.56
12	—	—	—	—	—	—	—	—	—	—	—	—
13	42.3	—	.46	—	2.0	1.9	20.9	907	.0318	2.60	0.65	0.25
14	46.8	—	.46	—	2.5	2.3	25.9	944	.0309	3.00	0.75	0.66
15	7.7	—	9.09	—	0.5	—	5.5	430	—	0.50	0.18	0.22
16	—	—	9.09	—	0.5	5.9	6.4	436	—	0.40	0.13	0.17
17	—	—	—	—	—	—	—	—	—	—	—	—
18	—	—	—	—	—	—	—	—	—	—	—	—
19	6.4	—	5.46	—	0.5	5.5	18.6	205	—	0.22	0.12	0.15
20	20.5	—	2.23	—	1.4	6.2	9.9	1265	—	3.19	0.74	0.83
21	12.3	182	.96	—	1.3	7.3	13.2	1270	—	2.93	0.65	0.69
22	20.5	—	1.50	—	1.3	6.8	10.0	1241	—	3.18	0.72	0.73
23	60.5	—	6.14	—	2.1	14.1	84.5	855	—	0.59	0.17	0.25
24	14.1	—	5.73	—	0.6	4.5	21.8	495	—	0.40	0.19	0.26
25	68.2	—	18.41	—	1.0	5.9	44.5	654	—	0.69	0.21	0.32
26	12.7	—	6.00	—	0.5	5.0	25.9	455	—	0.31	0.15	0.22
27	1.4	—	.09	—	12.3	20.0	4.5	622	.0105	0.97	0.19	0.30
28	17.7	—	—	—	16.8	49.5	203.6	1811	—	3.23	0.70	0.50

NOTE: Information in this table was reproduced from Nutrient Requirements of Poultry, 7th revised ed., (1977), pages 42-45, with the permission of the National Academy of Sciences, Washington, D.C.

TABLE 22   SUGGESTED FORMAT FOR FORMULA CHARTS

Formula __#16__   Type of Ration __Complete Holding, Corn Base__   Calorie:Protein Ratio __110__

Ing. #	Ingredient	% in Mix	Protein %	Protein Amt.	Met. Energy kcal/lb	Met. Energy Amt.	Calcium %	Calcium Amt.	Total P %	Total P Amt.	Avail. P %	Avail. P Amt.
5	Corn, yellow	.618	.088	.5435	1559	963.5	.0002	.000124	.0028	.0073	.0008	.00049
3	Barley	.25	.116	.029	1200	300	.0003	.000075	.0036	.0009	.0011	.00028
20	Soybean meal, solv. 50%	.072	.508	.03658	1131	81.4	.0029	.000209	.0065	.00047	.002	.00014
1	Alfalfa meal, dehy. 17%	.02	.175	.0035	623	12.5	.0144	.000288	.0022	.00004	.0022	.00004
7	Dicalcium phosphate, 18.5%	.015					.21	.00315	.185	.00278	.185	.00278
12	Limestone flour	.01					.38	.0038				
18	Salt, iodized	.005										
V/M	Vitamin:mineral premix	.01										
T		1.000		.12343		1357.4		.007646		.00592		.00373

Ing. #	Vit. A IU/lb	Vit. A Amt.	Vit. D ICU/lb	Vit. D Amt.	Riboflavin mg/lb	Riboflavin Amt.	Total Niacin mg/lb	Total Niacin Amt.	Lysine %	Lysine Amt.	Methionine %	Methionine Amt.	Cystine %	Cystine Amt.
5	1318	815			.455	.281	10.9	6.74	.0024	.0015	.0020	.00124	.0015	.00093
3					.80	.2	25	6.25	.004	.001	.0017	.00043	.0019	.00048
20					1.4	.101	9.9	.71	.0319	.0023	.0074	.00053	.0083	.0006
1	83909	1618			6.18	.124	17.3	.35	.0073	.0001	.0023	.00005	.002	.00004
7														
12														
18														
V/M	300000	3000	40000	400	150	1.5	1500	15						
T		4993		400		2.206		19.05		.0049		.00225		.00205

APPENDIX B

Symptoms of Vitamin and Mineral Deficiencies in Geese

Vitamin	Deficiency Symptoms*
VITAMIN A	Retarded growth; general weakness; staggering gait; ruffled plumage; low resistance to infections and internal parasites; eye infection; lowered production and fertility; increased mortality. (Adult birds develop symptoms slower than goslings.) *Sources:* Fish-liver oils, yellow corn, alfalfa meal, fresh greens.
VITAMIN D_3	Retarded growth; rickets; birds walk as little as possible, and when they do move, their gait is unsteady and stiff; bills become soft and rubbery and are easily bent; thin-shelled eggs; reduced egg production; bones of wings and legs are fragile and easily broken; hatchability is lowered. *Sources:* Sunlight, fish-liver oils, synthetic sources.
VITAMIN E	Unsteady gait; goslings suddenly become prostrated, lying with legs stretched out behind, head retracted over the back; head weaves from side to side; reduced hatchability of eggs; high mortality in newly hatched goslings; sterility in males and reproductive failure in hens. *Sources:* Many feedstuffs both of plant and animal origin, particularly alfalfa meal, rice polish and bran, distiller's dried corn solubles, wheat middlings.
VITAMIN K	Delayed clotting of blood; internal or external hemorrhaging which may result in birds bleeding to death from even small wounds. *Sources:* Fish meal, meat meal, alfalfa meal, fresh greens.
THIAMINE	Loss of appetite; sluggishness; emaciation; head tremors; convulsions; head retracted over the back. *Sources:* Grains and grain by-products.

RIBOFLAVIN Diarrhea; retarded growth; curled-toe paralysis; drooping wings; birds fall back on their hocks; eggs hatch poorly.

Sources: Dried yeast, skim milk, whey, alfalfa meal, green feeds.

NIACIN Retarded growth; leg weakness; bowed legs; enlarged hocks; diarrhea; poor feather development.

Sources: Dried yeast and synthetic sources. (Most of the niacin in cereal grains is unavailable to poultry.)

BIOTIN Bottoms of feet are rough and calloused, with bleeding cracks; lesions develop in corners of mouth, spreading to area around the bill; eyelids eventually swell and stick shut; slipped tendon (see also choline and manganese deficiencies); eggs hatch poorly.

Sources: Most feedstuffs, but especially dried yeast, whey, meat and bone meal, skim milk, alfalfa meal, soybean meal, green feeds. (The biotin in wheat and barley is mostly unavailable to poultry. If raw eggs are fed to animals, avidin — a protein in the egg-white — binds biotin, making it unavailable.)

PANTOTHENIC Retarded growth; viscous discharge causes eyelids to be-
ACID come granular and stick together; rough-looking feathers; scabs in corners of mouth and around vent; bottoms of feet rough and calloused, but lesions are seldom as severe as in a biotin deficiency; drop in egg production; reduced hatchability of eggs; poor liveability of newly hatched goslings.

Sources: All major feedstuffs, particularly brewer's and torula yeast, whey, skim and buttermilk, fish solubles, wheat bran, alfafa meal.

CHOLINE Retarded growth; slipped tendon (see also biotin and manganese deficiencies).

Sources: Most feedstuffs but especially fish meal, meat meal, soybean meal, cottonseed meal, wheat germ meal. (Evidence indicates that choline is synthesized by mature birds in quantities adequate for egg production.)

VITAMIN B_6 Poor appetites; extremely slow growth; nervousness; convulsions; jerky head movements; goslings run about aimlessly, sometimes rolling over on their backs and rapidly paddling their feet; increased mortality.

Sources: Grains and seeds.

FOLACIN | Retarded growth; poor feathering; colored feathers show a band of faded color; reduced egg production; decline in hatchability; occasionally slipped tendon.

Sources: Green feeds, fish meal, meat meal.

VITAMIN B$_{12}$ | Poor hatchability; high mortality in newly hatched goslings; retarded growth; poor feathering; degenerated gizzards; occasionally slipped tendon.

Sources: Animal products and synthetic sources.

Mineral	Deficiency Symptoms*

CALCIUM AND PHOSPHORUS | Rickets; retarded growth; increased mortality; in rare cases, thin-shelled eggs.

Sources: Calcium — oyster shells and limestone. Phosphorus — dicalcium phosphate, soft rock phosphate, bone meal, meat and bone meal, fish meal. (Most all feedstuffs have varying amounts of calcium and phosphorus, but typically only about one-third of the phosphorus in plant products is available to birds.)

MAGNESIUM | Goslings go into brief convulsions and then lapse into a coma from which they usually recover if they are not swimming; rapid decline in egg production.

Sources: Most feedstuffs, especially limestone, meat and bone meal, grain brans. (Raising either the calcium or phosphorus content of feed magnifies a deficiency of this mineral.)

MANGANESE | Slipped tendon in one or both legs; retarded growth; weak egg shells; reduced egg production and hatchability. Slipped tendon (also known as perosis) is first evidenced by the swelling and flattening of the hock joint, followed by the Achilles tendon slipping from its condyles (groove), causing the lower leg to project out to the side of the body at a severe angle. (Perosis can also be the result of biotin or choline deficiencies.)

Sources: Most feedstuffs, especially manganese sulfate, rice bran, limestone, oyster shell, wheat middlings and bran.

CHLORIDE

Extremely slow growth; high mortality; unnatural nervousness.

Sources: Most feedstuffs, especially animal products, beet molasses, alfalfa meal.

COPPER AND IRON

Anemia.

Sources: Most feedstuffs, including fresh greens.

IODINE

Goiter (enlargement of the thyroid gland); decreased hatchability of eggs.

Sources: Iodine. Iodized salt contains such small quantities of iodine that it cannot be relied upon to provide sufficient iodine.

POTASSIUM

Rare, but when it occurs, results in retarded growth and high mortality.

Sources: Most feedstuffs.

SODIUM

Poor growth; cannibalism; decreased egg production.

Sources: Most feedstuffs, but especially salt and animal products.

ZINC

Retarded growth; moderately to severely frayed feathers; enlarged hock joints; slipped tendon.

Sources: Zinc oxide and most feedstuffs, especially animal products.

Summarized in part from *Nutrient Requirements of Poultry,* 7th revised edition (1977), pages 11-20, with the permission of the National Academy of Sciences, Washington, D.C.

*The deficiency symptoms are given in the sequence they normally evidence themselves.

APPENDIX C

Predators

Adult geese are large enough that they are not lost to predators as frequently as smaller and weaker fowl such as chickens and ducks. However, geese of all ages are not immune to attack as some people seem to think. Dogs, coyote, foxes, bobcats, raccoons and large owls — among others — can mangle and kill geese. Because wild animals are essential in preserving the delicate balance of the natural world, we should not attempt to eliminate them, but rather, need to give our poultry sufficient protection so that hungry predators will not be able to dine at the expense of our birds.

SECURITY MEASURES

Because many predators have nocturnal habits and waterfowl roost on the ground, geese are most vulnerable at night when they will run in circles or pile into corners when spooked, if a pond isn't available. A fenced yard or a building where geese can be locked in after dark is a must in most localities.

A sturdy woven wire fence at least four feet high goes a long way in keeping geese safe while they rest. In areas where determined and agile hunters, such as fox and raccoon are present, electric fencing can be used in combination with woven wire fences to make yards safer after sundown. To be most effective, two strands of electric wire need to be utilized. One strand should run around the outside of the woven wire four inches above the ground, while the second strand should be installed several inches above the top of the fence.

If weasels, mink, owls and cats are prevalent, at nighttime it will be expedient to pen your goslings in a shelter having a covered top as well as sturdy sides. Some predators will dig under fences or dirt floors of buildings to gain access to impenned birds. Burying the bottom six to twelve inches of fences that encircle yards or covering the floor of goosehouses with wire netting will keep out excavators.

Because goslings and setting geese are especially vulnerable to predation, extra care must be taken to provide them with secure quarters. Setting geese should be encouraged to nest in covered nests that are situated in fenced yards.

IDENTIFYING THE CULPRIT

If you do lose birds or eggs, it is helpful to be able to identify the culprit in order to prevent future pilfering. Once predators discover a convenient source of food, they often return at regular intervals if permitted to do so.

Crows, Jays, Magpies and Gulls

Telltale Signs — Punctured eggs or shells scattered around the base of an elevated perch, such as a fencepost or tree stump. These birds also occasionally steal newly hatched goslings.

Stopping Losses — Provide covered nest boxes and gather eggs several times a day. Keep goslings in wire-covered runs until they are ten to fourteen days old.

Hawks

Telltale Signs — Goslings disappear during daylight without a trace or only a few scattered feathers or clumps of down. Hawks are probably falsely accused of stealing poultry more often than any other predator. Because the large, soaring hawks (buteos) are so highly visible, people mistakenly assume these winged hunters are the cause of every barnyard fowl that comes up missing. Actually, the hawks we need to worry about are the ones that are seldom seen by the casual observer: the accipiter family which includes the Goshawk, Cooper's Hawk and Sharp-shinned Hawk. The accipiters are secretive — sticking to trees — and hunt from low altitudes. They can be identified by their short, round wings and long tails. If you do on occasion lose goslings to hawks, your frustration may be reduced if you'll remember that the average hawk destroys a minimum of 200 to 300 rodents annually.

Stopping Losses — Keep goslings in wire-covered runs until they are several weeks old.

Owls

Telltale Signs —One or more birds killed nightly with head and neck eaten.

Stopping Losses — At night, lock goslings in a shelter covered with 1" x 1" wire netting. Some of the smaller species, such as Screech Owls can squeeze through 2" x 2" wire mesh. When game is scarce during severe winter weather, large species such as the Great Horned Owl will occasionally attack fully grown geese.

Dogs

Telltale Signs — A number of geese, sometimes the entire flock, badly maimed. Check for large holes under or through fences, and clumps of dog hair caught on wire. In most localities, dogs are the worst enemy of the domestic goose.

Stopping Losses — Strong woven wire fences at least four feet high topped with several strands of barbed wire. Dogs will dig under fences if the soil is relatively soft, so a strand of electric fence several inches above ground level around the outside of fences may be in order.

Cats

Telltale Signs — Crushed eggs held together by shell membranes. Goslings disappear without a trace, or only a few feathers are found in a secluded spot where the animal fed.

Stopping Losses — Keep goslings in wire-covered runs until they are several weeks old. Domestic cats are intelligent enough that they can be taught fairly easily not to molest poultry. When a pet cat is seen stalking your birds, let the tabby know immediately that the goslings are off limits. Throwing a rolled up newspaper at the offending animal will usually get the message across. If you have problems with stray cats, a live trap may be needed.

Foxes

Telltale Signs — Foxes are fastidious hunters and normally leave little evidence of their visits. Usually they kill just one bird per visit and take their victim with them or partially bury it nearby. You might be able to find a small hole under or through fences, or a poorly fitted gate or door pushed ajar.

Stopping Losses — Tight fencing at least four feet high with two strands of barbed or electric wire, and close-fitting gates. Foxes will squeeze or dig under fences that are not flush with the ground.

Raccoons

Telltale Signs — Ends of eggs bitten off or crops (esophagus) eaten out of dead birds — possibly heads missing. Usually returns every fourth or fifth night, sometimes more frequently.

Stopping Losses — Fences four feet high with two strands of electric wire, or lock birds at night in shelter with top and sides.

Skunks

Telltale Signs — Destroyed nest with crushed shells mixed with nest debris.

Stopping Losses — Gather eggs daily. Encourage setting geese to nest in fenced yards.

Opposum

Telltale Signs — Smashed eggs and goslings that are badly mauled.

Stopping Losses — Gather eggs daily, and at night lock goslings in a shelter covered with a top.

Mink and Weasels

Telltale Signs — Young goslings disappear or larger birds killed, evidently for amusement, with small teeth marks on head and neck.

Stopping Losses — At night, lock goslings in a shelter that is covered with ½-inch wire hardware cloth. As incredible as it seems, mink and weasels can pass through holes as small as one inch in diameter.

Rats

Telltale Signs — Eggs or dead goslings pulled into underground tunnels.

Stopping Losses — Until goslings are four weeks old, at night put them in a pen that has sides, top and floor that are covered with ½-inch wire mesh. Rat populations should be kept under control with cats, traps or poison.

Snapping Turtles and Large Fish

Telltale Signs — Goslings disappear mysteriously while swimming.

Stopping Losses — If your geese frequent bodies of water that host turtles or large fish, such as northern pike and large mouth bass, keep goslings away from the water until they are two weeks old.

APPENDIX D

Goose Recipes

Goose meat and eggs can be made into a variety of tasty and nutritious dishes. Since most cookbooks give little consideration to waterfowl cookery, Millie and I would like to share a dozen of our favorite recipes. We hope you'll enjoy them as much as our family and friends do.

POTATO QUICHE

- Stir together in 9-inch pan:
  2½-3 cups shredded raw potato
    3 tbsp. rendered goose fat or veg. oil
- Press into crust shape.
- Bake at 425° for 15 minutes; remove from oven.
- Layer on:
  1-1½ cups grated Swiss or cheddar cheese
  ½-1 cup diced, cooked goose
  ¼-½ cup sliced onion
  ¼-½ cup chopped sweet pepper
- Beat together:
  1¼ cups goose eggs
  ¾ cup milk
  ½ tsp. salt
- Pour egg mixture over other ingredients.
- Sprinkle with: 1 tbsp. parsley flakes.
- Return to oven and bake at 425° for 20 to 25 minutes or until lightly browned.
- Serves 3 to 5.

GOOSE CROQUETTES

- Combine:
  1-1½ cups cooked goose, chopped
  ½ cup white sauce or leftover gravy
  ¾-1 cup bread crumbs
  1-2 tbsp. parsley
  1 tbsp. onion, minced
- Form into croquettes, roll in fine cracker or dried bread crumbs.
- Fry in oil over medium heat until lightly browned.
- Serve with gravy if desired.
- Serves 4 to 6.

ROAST GOOSE

> goose
> salt
> dressing, if desired

- For stuffed bird, fill body and neck cavity. Fasten neck skin to back with a skewer. Tie legs together.
- If unstuffed, sprinkle body cavity lightly with salt.
- Place goose, breast side up, on rack in shallow roasting pan.
- Roast uncovered for 45 minutes to 1 hour in 400° oven.
- Spoon off accumulated fat at ½ hour intervals.
- Reduce oven temperature to 325° and continue roasting in covered pan. Allow 10 to 12 minutes per pound of bird (unstuffed geese will take slightly less time).

GIBLET-SAGE DRESSING

- Cook giblets in small saucepan with enough water to cover. Cook until tender, then chop.
- Pour liquid (½ to ¾ cup stock, water or milk) over:
  > 9 cups toasted bread crumbs
  > 2½ tsp. salt
  > ½ tsp. pepper
  > 3-4 tsp. sage
- Mix well, place in greased casserole or stuff goose.
- Bake at 375° for 45 to 50 minutes (for casserole).
- Serves 4 to 6.

SAUERKRAUT DRESSING

- Sauté:
  > 6 tbsp. goose drippings or oil
  > 1½ cups onions, chopped
- Add:
  > 2 quarts sauerkraut, drained
- Simmer 15 minutes, stirring once or twice.
- Transfer to large bowl and cool.
- Add:
  > 2 cups tart apples, chopped
  > 1 cup raw potato, shredded
  > 2 tsp. caraway seeds (optional)
  > ¼ tsp. pepper
- Mix lightly.
- Fill goose cavity.

STIR-FRIED VEGETABLES WITH GOOSE

- Prepare raw vegetables (enough to make 5 cups) such as: asparagus, broccoli, cabbage, carrots, cauliflower, green beans or squash, in your choice of combination.
- Group vegetables according to their cooking time and set aside.
- Heat in large skillet:
  - 4 tbsp. cooking oil
- Sauté:
  - 2-3 cloves garlic, minced
  - 1 large onion, wedged
- Add:
  - ¾-1 cup leftover goose, cut in strips or chunks
- Stir-fry over medium-high heat for 3 to 5 minutes.
- Add longest cooking vegetables such as cabbage and carrots, continuing to stir-fry. As soon as they begin to tenderize, add faster cooking vegetables. If necessary, add more oil.
- Add sunflower seeds, sesame seeds and/or small chunks of jicama root
- When vegetables are crispy-tender and still have their bright colors, serve immediately over hot rice.
- Serve with soy sauce sprinkled on top of vegetables.
  Note: Have other meal preparations finished when you begin stir-frying, since this will take a lot of last minute work.

GOOSE BARLEY STEW

- Sauté:
  - 2 tbsp. rendered goose fat
  - 1 clove garlic, minced
  - 1 cup onion, chopped
- Add:
  - 5 cups vegetable stock or water
  - 1 tsp. salt
  - goose giblets, neck, back and wings (or carcass)
- Cover and cook for 1 hour. Remove meat and bones. Cut up meat and return to kettle.
- Add:
  - 1 pint tomatoes
  - 1 cup carrot chunks
  - 1½ cups coarsely shredded cabbage
  - 1 cup pearl barley (noodles or rice may be substituted)
  - ½ tsp. each of summer savory and parsley, or other desired herbs
- Simmer for 40 minutes.
- Add:
  - ½ cup celery, diced
  - 1 cup peas, fresh or frozen
- Cook 20 minutes.
- Serve with fresh bread or biscuits.

PAPA'S STOVETOP SOUFFLÉ

        2 cups milk
        ½ cup cheese, grated
        1⅓ cups goose eggs (approximately 3 eggs)
        2 tbsp. flour
        salt or pepper to season as desired
- Heat milk in saucepan over medium heat.
- Melt cheese in milk.
- Beat eggs thoroughly, then add flour to eggs and mix well.
- Add egg mixture to hot milk; stir to mix.
- Cook over low heat for 20 to 25 minutes until done.
- Serve immediately.
- Serves 4 to 5.

HOMEMADE NOODLES

        4 cups flour*
        1 cup eggs (either whole eggs or egg yolks)
        water
- Add beaten eggs to flour and work in.
- Add sufficient water to make pliable dough. Knead for 5 to 10 minutes.
- Cover and let rest for 20 minutes.
- Roll out very thinly with rolling pin or pasta machine.
- Hang over clothes rack and let dry slightly.
- Cut in desired widths.
- Finish drying.
- Package and store in freezer.

* May use all whole wheat flour, half whole wheat and half unbleached white, or any other combination you desire.

DEVILED GOOSE EGGS

        4 goose eggs
        ¼ tsp. salt
        ⅛ tsp. pepper
        1-2 tsp. mustard
        4-5 tbsp. mayonnaise
        4 tsp. vinegar
- Put eggs in saucepan, cover with water, put on lid and bring to a boil.
- Cook 10 minutes.
- Turn off heat, leave pan on burner, covered, for 10 to 15 minutes.
- Cool and shell eggs.
- Cut eggs in half lengthwise. Remove yolks and mash.
- Add remaining ingredients.
- Refill whites.
- Garnish with parsley or paprika.

BAKED EGG CUSTARD

> 2 goose eggs
> ½ cup sugar or ⅓ cup honey
> 4 cups milk, scalded
> 1 tsp. vanilla
> nutmeg (optional)

- Beat eggs slightly.
- Add sugar and vanilla (if using honey, add to scalded milk).
- Pour milk slowly over egg mixture. Stir until thoroughly mixed.
- Pour into lightly greased casserole dish.
- Sprinkle with nutmeg.
- Set dish in flat pan containing 1 inch hot water.
- Bake 50 minutes at 325°.
- Serves 6 to 8.

CORNMEAL WAFFLES

> 1½ cups yellow cornmeal
> ¼ cup whole wheat flour
> ⅓ tsp. salt
> ½ tsp. baking soda
> 1 tsp. baking powder
> 1 goose egg, separated
> 2 cups yogurt or buttermilk
> ½ cup goose fat (rendered) or oil

- Measure cornmeal, flour, salt, baking soda, and baking powder into mixing bowl. Stir to blend.
- Beat egg yolk slightly and combine with yogurt or buttermilk.
- Add to cornmeal mixture, beating with a spoon until smooth. Stir in fat.
- Beat egg-white until stiff and fold into batter.
- Bake in waffle iron until outside is brown and crisp.
- Serve with goose gravy, fruit syrup or honey.
- Delicious for breakfast, lunch or supper.

APPENDIX E

Using Feathers and Down

It's not unheard of for a goose flock to be kept chiefly for the luxurious plumage these birds produce. With their unmatched combination of light weight and warmth retaining ability, the down and small body feathers of geese are considered the ultimate natural filler for cold weather clothing and bedding. From the large, stiff-quilled feathers of the body and wings, a number of useful and interesting items can also be crafted, including homemade arrows, shuttlecocks, dusters and old-fashioned writing pens. All geese produce quality feathers, although some people claim that those from European breeds (especially Embdens) are superior. When butchered and plucked cleanly, medium to large birds typically yield a total of ⅓ to ½ pound of dry feathers.

PLUCKING LIVE GEESE

In conversations pertaining to goose feathers, a frequently asked question concerns the advisability of plucking live birds. Some breeders and waterfowl literature strongly condemn this practice as being cruel. The basic arguments against it are that feathers consist primarily of protein and their replacement is a drain on the birds; and, "How would you like to have your hair pulled out by its roots several times a year?" While I have never encouraged live plucking, I'll try to present the facts and let you decide your own opinion.

Geese naturally replace their garb yearly during a molt that takes a month or longer to complete. Feathers are mostly protein. However, work done at a goose research center in France indicates that, once the breeding season is over, mature geese that are well fed can be live picked, without apparent negative results, every seven weeks up until several weeks before cold weather sets in. The study also concluded that if properly fed, young geese that are well feathered can be plucked once every seven weeks up until three to five weeks prior to being butchered.

The actual physical discomfort that geese experience when small, mature feathers are extracted is hard to determine. If new feathers that are still growing are pulled, bleeding can occur and birds normally flinch noticeably, indicating that it hurts. However, comparing the pulling of down and breast feathers with the removal of human hair is probably inaccurate since mature feathers are attached to the skin by a relatively weak bond and do not have true roots.

Should you decide to live pluck your geese, taking the following precautions will greatly reduce the possibility of your birds suffering ill effects.
- Take feathers only from the underside of the goose.
- Pull out only small pinches of feathers and down at a time to keep from tearing the bird's skin.
- Remove a maximum of 50 percent of the plumage from the plucked area, and don't leave any bare patches.

PILLOWS

To keep feathers from working their way out of pillows and tickling your nose, a tightly woven cloth such as down-proof ticking is essential. Double stitching the seams is imperative in keeping the exits closed.

Pillows filled solely with down retain their shape poorly. To make them more resilient, pillows need to be filled with a combination of down and small, soft body feathers. Many people find a ratio of 75 percent down to 25 percent feathers to be just right, while others prefer a firmer mixture of fifty to fifty. The quantity of filler required depends on pillow size and personal preference. Do keep in mind that feathers pack together considerably. As with all feather filled products, feather pillows need to be fluffed frequently to maintain their spring and to keep the stuffing evenly distributed.

COMFORTERS, QUILTS, SLEEPING BAGS AND CLOTHING

The tops and bottoms of comforters, quilts and sleeping bags must be lined with down-proof material. Channels five to six inches wide should be used to help keep the down and feathers evenly distributed. Leave one end of the channels open for stuffing.

When the stiff quilled plumes of the wings, tail and body have been kept separate at picking time, the down and small body feathers can be used in the ratio they come off of the birds. As each channel is filled, sew the opening shut by hand, and then cap the edges with binding.

Jacket with channels to keep down evenly distributed.

The making of down-filled mittens, booties, vests, jackets and parkas is an enjoyable winter activity that provides fine gifts for family members and friends. Be sure to use down-proof lining and make all seams double to keep the down from escaping. For parkas, vests, etc., the channels should be approximately two to three inches wide. To keep large pieces of clothing as lightweight as possible, use 75 to 90 percent down, with small quantities of body feathers for loft.

APPENDIX F

Using Geese as Weeders

Geese by the thousands are annually employed to control unwanted plant growth in a variety of crops, as well as along fence rows and around out buildings. This unique partnership between man and fowl is made possible because geese eat numerous types of noxious grasses and broad-leaf weeds, but find various cultivated plants disagreeable to their palate. While many of today's agriculturists are increasing their reliance on chemical herbicides rather than seeking methods of working harmoniously with nature, weeder geese do continue to be utilized successfully by a good number of nurseries, orchards, homesteaders and truck and general farmers.

When managed properly, these feathered herbivores have a number of advantages over mechanical and chemical means of checking weed growth. Geese do not disturb the roots of crop plants nor leave behind toxic residue. They nip off weeds that grow among the desired plants, continue working rain or shine and fertilize as they go. However, to avoid being disappointed, you shouldn't expect geese to be a magical cure for all weed problems. Rather, they should be looked upon as a useful aid in reducing unwanted plant growth in specific crops. Upon hearing that these birds can be used as weeders, people sometimes make the mistake of turning geese loose in their gardens assuming they instinctively know which plants are weeds and which are not.

SUITABLE BREEDS

Conceivably, any variety of geese could be used for weeding since all eat grass and weeds. However, light to mediumweight birds are usually preferred since they tend to be better foragers and are less likely to trample plants. Of all breeds, the Chinese is by far the most popular for weeding chores due to their active foraging ability, moderate size, unmatched agility, good availability and reasonable price.

BEST AGE FOR WEEDING

Geese of most ages can be enlisted for weeding, but young birds have a number of advantages when used in row crops. Goslings are smaller and therefore less likely to tread on tender plants, they have voracious appetites that keep them on the move, and when hungry are less inclined to nibble on crop plants because they are more selective in their tastes than older geese. Under commercial conditions, five to six weeks is generally considered the youngest age that goslings can safely be placed in fields. But for the small producer who can keep an eye on the birds and put them under shelter in case of rain, goslings can be put to work several weeks earlier when the weather is mild, especially if they are being brooded naturally.

NUMBER NEEDED

The number of weeders needed depends on factors such as time of year, climate, crop, volume of noxious vegetation that is present when the birds are put to work and whether or not the middles of rows are mechanically tilled. In most cultivated crops, if geese are placed in the field before there is a heavy growth of unwanted grass and broad leaf plants, two to four birds per acre are normally sufficient. In uncultivated fields, approximately twice as many geese will be required.

FENCING

To be effective, geese must be confined to the area they are working. For temporary fencing, poultry netting — eighteen to twenty-four inches high for goslings, thirty-six inches for mature geese — can be installed by wiring it to wooden or steel stakes that are driven into the ground at ten- to fifteen-foot intervals. A single strand of electric wire installed eight to ten inches above ground level has also been used successfully with geese that are six weeks or older.

DRINKING WATER

Thirsty geese are not efficient workers. Waterers should be provided that supply adequate capacity so the birds are not frequently left dry. The location of the drinking water is also important since it controls the movement of the geese. To encourage birds to cover large areas evenly, it is sometimes necessary to place water receptacles at opposite ends of a field.

FEEDING

Weeder geese must be hungry most of the time if they are to work effectively. However, it is recommended that a small amount of complete pellets or a mixture of pellets and grain be fed once a day in the evening to keep the birds in a strong, healthy condition. Grains alone do not supply a balanced diet under most circumstances. The quantity of feed that should be fed depends on the age and size of the birds and the availability of palatable grasses and weeds. When edible greens are plentiful, a pound or less of feed per ten birds should do, while two to three pounds may be called for when fields are nearly clean. The appearance of weak or slow-moving birds is often an indication that more feed is needed. Keep in mind that geese will starve to death rather than eat some types of extremely tough or strong-flavored vegetation.

SHADE

To prevent sunstroke, geese of all ages must have shade during warm weather. If natural protection from the sun doesn't exist in the working area, some type of simple shelter should be erected that provides adequate shade for all of the birds to rest under at one time.

PROTECTION FROM PREDATORS

It's difficult to fence large working areas well enough to keep out all hungry meat-eaters. Since a majority of raids by predators are carried out between sundown and sunup, weeders, especially young ones, should be closed at nighttime in a building or yard that is tightly fenced with wire at least four feet high. When locked up at night, a minimum of four to five square feet should be allowed per bird.

SPRAYS, FERTILIZERS AND BAITS

If insecticides, herbicides, fertilizers or slug baits are applied in areas where weeder geese are working, the birds should always be removed for at least two or three days, or until the fertilizer has dissolved or bait has been removed. Geese can consume small quantities of some sprays without obvious ill effects. However, toxic substances can accumulate in their body tissues and be passed to unsuspecting humans if the contaminated birds are butchered for meat or used for the production of eating eggs. It is always better to be overly precautious in this matter rather than taking a chance of losing birds, or worse yet, of polluting the food of family, friends or customers.

APPENDIX G
Show Time

Agricultural fairs just wouldn't be complete without rows of cackling chickens, quacking ducks and honking geese. North American poultry breeders have been displaying their fowl at public exhibits for over 130 years. By digging into the annals of poultry history, one finds that back in 1849, the first exclusive show was held November 14, at the Public Gardens in Boston, Massachusetts. An interesting note — the Boston Poultry Exposition continues as an annual event.

Poultry shows serve a number of useful functions. First, they provide a meeting place for old and new friends who share a common interest. Second, they allow the public to see and enjoy the breeder's skills. Third, they give opportunity to compare one's stock and ideas with those of other breeders.

In most North American shows, birds are judged by comparison and then placed 1st, 2nd, 3rd, etc. However, I personally prefer and recommend the European system of judging, which grades the entrants: poor, fair, good, excellent, or by some similar scale. The grading system moves the emphasis away from competing against other breeders to striving to improve one's own stock. This method also helps the less experienced breeder know the true quality of her or his birds. (It is important to keep in mind that judges do make mistakes and they can only evaluate the external features of birds — which is just part of the picture since productivity is also essential.) Unfortunately, under the placing system it is quite common for mediocre specimens to win first prizes due to weak competition, encouraging novice owners to think they have better birds than they actually do.

WHO CAN SHOW?

The majority of poultry shows are open to anyone who wants to enter their birds. Except for the occasional specialty club show, belonging to a local or national organization is usually not a prerequisite for exhibiting your geese. Ordinarily, to help cover expenses and provide premiums, there is a minimal entry fee. In some states, any fowl that is shown from out of state must be blood tested for Pullorum-Typhoid (see Chapter 11). A few states even require the test for instate birds. Premium lists normally spell out such requirements.

WHAT CAN BE SHOWN?

Any healthy goose of a standard breed can be shown. Presently, the breeds that are officially recognized are the Egyptian, Canada, Chinese, Tufted Roman, Pilgrim, Sebastopol, Pomeranian, American Buff, African, Embden and Toulouse. Crossbreeds are sometimes seen at fairs. Except in 4-H or FFA categories, entering such geese normally is a waste of time since they usually are disqualified because there is no standard for judging them.

HOW ARE BIRDS ENTERED?

To exhibit birds in a show, you need a copy of the premium list and an entry blank. For county, provincial and state fair premium lists and entry blanks, contact your local agriculture extension specialist. For other shows, check with established poultry breeders in your area and look over advertisements for shows in the Poultry Press and Feather Fancier (see Appendix J). Normally, entry forms must be filled out and returned to the show secretary anywhere from one to four weeks prior to the show date, so you'll need to plan ahead. To avoid being disqualified, be sure to read and follow all instructions as outlined in the premium list.

A superb Sebastopol old female on exhibit at the annual Ohio National Poultry Show. Bred and exhibited by the late W. C. Garber.

Shows normally have separate classes for old ganders, old geese, young ganders and young geese. Be careful to enter birds of the correct sex and age in the appropriate class. Birds that are exhibited need to be tagged with numbered leg bands and these numbers recorded on the entry blank.

PREPARING GEESE FOR EXHIBITION

To show to their best advantage, geese must be clean, in good feather, carrying the correct amount of weight and accustomed to being penned in a restricted inclosure. Birds that are dirty, in poor feather condition or are over or underweight will fair poorly under most judges, even if they are excellent specimens otherwise. Also, while appraising geese, judges have little patience with birds that thrash wildly about or crouch in the corner of their cages.

Cage Training

For geese that have always had the freedom to run in a spacious pasture or yard, being locked up in a display cage can be a frightening experience. The first phase in training geese for exhibition is to work gently and quietly when near the birds and talk to them with a calm, reassuring voice at feeding time.

A well conditioned Dewlap Toulouse old female shown by Steve Langer, Sherwood, Oregon.

Several weeks prior to the show date — for birds that have never been exhibited — it's a good practice to coop them individually in cages that are at least 3' x 3' x 3' for two or three days with food and drinking water.

Conditioning

Fortunately, geese are neat birds and will clean themselves if given half a chance. Seldom do they need to be hand washed prior to a show — except possibly to tidy the bill, feet or a few soiled feathers with warm water and a soft brush or sponge. Three of the worst enemies of show geese are mud, grease and excessive exposure to sunlight, which can cause the plumage to fade, dry out and lose its sheen.

TRANSPORTING GEESE TO SHOWS

Some thought should be given as to how you will get your geese to the show in good feather and mental condition. Occasionally someone will pull up to an exhibition hall with a pickup full of trumpeting geese inclosed only by raised panels on the truck bed. I prefer to use well-ventilated wooden crates made for the occasion or discarded waxed cardboard or wooden produce boxes often available free or for a minimum charge from the produce manager of grocery stores or produce stands. Keep in mind that geese are large and have high body temperatures, so they can overheat and suffocate rather easily if not given sufficient ventilation. By using clean bedding and having only one or two geese per carton, your feathered friends should arrive at their destination rested and in clean garments.

FEEDING AND CARE AT THE SHOW

Many shows provide attendants who feed and water the birds throughout the duration of an exhibition. However, you should check ahead of time if this matter is not clarified in the premium list so you will not be caught without feed and water containers and feed if this service is not provided.

DEFINITIONS OF SHOW TERMS AND ABBREVIATIONS

There are a number of unfamiliar terms and abbreviations that are likely to be encountered when a novice exhibits geese. The most common include:

O.F. — Old Female; geese that are over one year
O.M. — Old Male; ganders that are over one year
Y.F. — Young Female; geese that are under one year
Y.M. — Young Male; ganders that are under one year
B.B. — Best of Breed
B.O.B. or B.O.S.B. — Best Opposite Sex of Breed
B.V. — Best of Variety
B.O.V. or B.O.S.V. — Best Opposite Sex of Variety
A.S.V. — All Standard Varieties
A.O.S.V. — All Other Standard Varieties
Disq. — Disqualified

APPENDIX H

Goose Breeders and Hatchery Guide

The Goose Breeders and Hatchery Guide was prepared to help you locate sources of geese. While this list is not exhaustive, it does contain most of the major breeders and hatcheries in North America. Please keep in mind that the information is dated, and details such as addresses, stock sold, etc., may change with time.

While attempts have been made to include only reliable sources, I am not endorsing the quality of stock or service given by these firms. Some hatcheries sell crossbred goslings under purebred labels. If you are interested in acquiring a specific breed, ask potential sources if they guarantee their stock to be pure-blooded. (When writing poultry breeders and hatcheries, have the courtesy to enclose a stamp for their reply.)

Three additional sources for addresses of goose breeders are the Feather Fancier and Poultry Press (see Appendix J for their addresses) and the breeders directory of the Society for Preservation of Poultry Antiquities. The directory is available from the society's secretary (James Rice, Route 3, Greenwood, Wisconsin 54437) for $5 per copy.

Code: Hatcheries with no asterisk offer production-bred stock, while those with one asterisk (*) sell standard-bred geese. Two asterisks (**) indicate that both production-bred and standard-bred birds are available.

California

Fruit's Weeder Geese, 19459 Avenue 144, Porterville, CA 93257—Ph. 209-784-2246
  Goslings in White Chinese and Toulouse.

Hockman's, 12659 Devonshire, San Diego, CA 92107—Ph. 714-222-6983
  Goslings in White Chinese; African; Embden and Toulouse.

Kirby & Edith Blohm, 54 Blanca Lane, Watsonville, CA 95076—Ph. 408-724-6743
  Goslings in White Chinese; African; Embden and Toulouse.

Metzer Hatchery, 25870 Old Stage Road, Gonzales, CA 93926—Ph. 408-679-2355
  Goslings in White Chinese; African; Embden and Toulouse.

Florida

Morris Farms & Hatcheries Inc., 18370 S.W. 232 St., Goulds, FL 33170—Ph. 305-271-8982
  Goslings in Embden and Toulouse.

Illinois

*Stephen F. Gerdes, Rt. 1, Toluca, IL 61369—Ph. 815-452-2534
Hatching eggs, goslings and mature stock in Canada; White, Brown Chinese; Egyptian; Tufted Roman; Buff; Pilgrim; Buff Pied, Saddle Back Pomeranian; Sebastopol; African; Embden and Toulouse.

Indiana

Rose's Hatchery, 1326 S. Michigan, South Bend, IN 44618—Ph. 219-232-4202
Goslings in Embden.

Schueler's Hatchery, P.O. Box 20, Preble, IN 46782—Ph. 219-547-4209
Goslings in Embden and Toulouse.

Iowa

Council Bluffs Hatchery, 901 W. Broadway, Council Bluffs, IA 51501—Ph. 712-323-7169
Goslings in Embden and Toulouse.

Owings Duck & Goose Hatchery, W. Hwy. 7, Storm Lake, IA 51588
Goslings in African; Embden and Toulouse.

Shiltz Goose Breeding Farm, Bancroft, IA 50517—Ph. 515-885-2435
Goslings in white and gray market birds.

Stork Hatchery, 233 S. Madison Avenue, Fredericksburg, IA—Ph. 319-237-5981
Goslings in Embden.

Tenhulzen Hatchery, 232 Avenue C, Box 318, Denison, IA 51442
Goslings in White Chinese; African; Embden and Toulouse.

Massachusetts

*Roger A. Sanford, 832 Pine Hill Road, South Westport, MA 02790—Ph. 617-636-2533
Hatching eggs and goslings in White, Brown Chinese; African and Standard Toulouse.

Minnesota

**Crow River Valley Goose Farm, Rt. 1, Box 35, Mayer, MN 55360—Ph. 612-657-2436
Goslings and mature stock in Canada; Tufted Roman; American Buff; Pilgrim; Pomeranian; African; Embden; Toulouse and Standard Toulouse.

*Duane Urch, Rt. 1, Owatonna, MN 55060—Ph. 507-451-6782
Hatching eggs, goslings and mature stock in Canada; White, Brown Chinese; Egyptian; Pilgrim; Buff Pied, Pomeranian; Sebastopol; White African; Embden and Standard Toulouse.

Leuze's Waterfowl Hatchery, Rt. 5, Willmar, MN 56201
Goslings in Embden and Toulouse.

Neubert Hatcheries, P.O. Box 1239, Mankato, MN 56001
Hatching eggs, goslings and mature stock in White Chinese; African; Embden and Toulouse.

North Valley Hatchery, Rt. 2, Harris, MN 55032—Ph. 612-674-7302
Goslings in Embden and Toulouse.

Pietrus Hatchery, 112 East Pine, Sleepy Eye, MN 56085—Ph. 507-794-3411
Goslings in Embden and Toulouse.

Sobania Hatchery, Rt. 6, Little Falls, MN 56345—Ph. 612-632-3030
Goslings in White Chinese; American Buff; African; Embden and Toulouse.

**Stromberg's, 50 Lakes Drive, Pine River, MN 56474—Ph. 218-543-4223
Hatching eggs and goslings in Canada; White, Brown Chinese; Buff; Pilgrim; Pomeranian; African; Embden and Toulouse.

**Sunny Creek Farm & Hatchery, Red Lake Falls, MN 56750—Ph. 218-253-2211
Hatching eggs, goslings and mature stock in Canada; White, Brown Chinese; Buff; Pilgrim; Pomeranian; Sebastopol; African; Embden; Toulouse and Standard Toulouse.

Wild Wings of Oneka, Rt. 2, Hugo, MN 55038—Ph. 612-439-4287
Goslings in Canada.

Missouri

Cackle Hatchery, P.O. Box 529, Lebanon, MO 65536—Ph. 417-532-4581
Goslings in White Chinese; African; Embden and Toulouse.

Heart of Missouri, P.O. Box 954, Columbia, MO 65205—Ph. 314-443-1671
Goslings in White Chinese; African; Embden and Toulouse.

*Zillich Poultry Breeding Farms, Rt. 1, Mercer, MO 64661—Ph. 816-875-2572
Hatching eggs and goslings in Pilgrim and Embden.

Nebraska

Lloyd's Quality Hatchery, 10th & Kansas St., Box 203, Superior, NB 68978
Goslings in Embden and Toulouse.

Norfolk Hatchery, 116-118 S. 3rd, Norfolk, NB 68701
Goslings in Embden and Toulouse.

Wragge Hatchery, Howells, NB 68641
Goslings in Embden.

North Dakota

Magic City Hatchery, P.O. Box 1771, Minot, ND 58701—Ph. 701-839-3726
Goslings in Embden and Toulouse.

Ohio

Pilgrim Goose Hatchery, Creek Road, Williamsfield, OH 44093
Goslings in Pilgrim.

Pruden Hatchery, P.O. Box 391, Geneva, OH 44041—Ph. 216-466-1773
Goslings in White Chinese; African; Embden and Toulouse.

Ridgeway Hatcheries, Inc., LaRue, OH 43332—Ph. 614-499-2163
Goslings in White Chinese; Embden and Toulouse.

**Ronson Farms, P.O. Box 12565, Columbus, OH 43212—Ph. 614-486-6219
Goslings and mature stock in Canada; White, Brown Chinese; Egyptian; Tufted Roman; Buff; Pilgrim; Pomeranian; Sebastopol; African; Embden; Toulouse and Standard Toulouse.

Oklahoma

Country Hatchery, Inc., P.O. Box 747, Wewoka, OK 74884—Ph. 405-257-6222
Goslings in Toulouse.

Oregon

*Bernard S. Lind, Rt. 1, Box 37, Umatilla, OR 97882
Hatching eggs and goslings in American Buff; Buff Pied; Sebastopol and African.

**Mother Hen Farm & Hatchery, P.O. Box 492, Corvallis, OR 97330—Ph. 503-753-8486
Hatching eggs, goslings and mature stock in White, Brown Chinese and Pilgrim.

**Northwest Farms, Inc., P.O. Box 3003, Portland, OR 97208—Ph. 503-653-0344
Hatching eggs, goslings and mature stock in Canada; White, Brown Chinese; Tufted Roman; American Buff; Pilgrim; Buff Pied, Pomeranian; Sebastopol; African; Embden; Toulouse and Standard Toulouse.

Pennsylvania

Clearview Stock Farm & Hatchery, Gratz, PA 17030—Ph. 717-365-3234
Goslings in White, Brown Chinese; Buff; African; Embden and Toulouse.

*Feather Edge Farm, Rt. 1, Cochranton, PA 16314
Hatching eggs, goslings and mature stock in Canada; White Chinese; Tufted Roman; Buff; Pilgrim; Pomeranian; Sebastopol and African.

Hoffman Hatchery, Gratz, PA 17030—Ph. 717-365-3407
Goslings in White Chinese; African; Embden and Toulouse.

**Willow Hill Farm & Hatchery, Rt. 1, Box 100, Richland, PA 17087—Ph. 717-933-4606
Goslings in White, Brown Chinese; American Buff; Pilgrim; Sebastopol; African; Embden and Toulouse.

South Dakota

Beverly's Goose Hatchery, Rt. 1, Box 58, Howard, SD 75349—Ph. 605-772-4303
Goslings in Embden and Toulouse.

Inman Hatcheries, 3000 Third Avenue S.E., Box 616, Aberdeen, SD 57401—Ph. 605-225-8122
Goslings in White Chinese; Embden and Toulouse.

Sunshine State Hatchery, 404 W. Pipestone Avenue, Flandreau, SD 57028
Goslings in Embden and Toulouse.

Washington

Harder's Hatchery, Rt. 101, Box 316, Ritzville, WA 99169—Ph. 509-659-1423
Goslings in Embden.

Wisconsin

Abendroth's Waterfowl Hatchery, Rt. 2, Box 200, Waterloo, WI 53594—Ph. 414-478-2053
Goslings in Canada; White, Brown Chinese; Buff; Pilgrim; Pomeranian; African; Embden and Toulouse.

*Halbach Poultry Farm, 305 S. Third St., Waterford, WI 53185—Ph. 414-534-6405
Goslings and mature stock in White, Brown Chinese; Tufted Roman; Buff; Pilgrim; Pomeranian; Sebastopol; African; Embden and Toulouse.

Hickory Ridge Farm, Rt. 1, Pardeeville, WI 53954
Goslings in Canada.

Canada

Anstey Electric Hatchery Ltd., 22nd St. & Avenue B, Saskatoon, Saskatchewan S7M 0P9—Ph. 664-2266
Goslings in Embden.

Berg's Poultry Farm & Hatchery, Box 603, Russel, Manitoba R0J 1W0
Goslings in Toulouse.

Miller Hatcheries Ltd., 260 Main St., Winnipeg, Manitoba R3C 1A9—Ph. 943-6541   (Branches in Regina, Saskatoon, North Battleford and Edmonton)
Goslings in Embden.

Smith Hatcheries Ltd., Box 523, Prince Albert, Saskatchewan—Ph. 306-764-5606
Goslings in Pilgrim.

Springhill Hatchery, Neepawa, Manitoba R0J 1H0
Goslings in Embden.

Webfoot Farm & Hatchery Ltd., Elora, Ontario N0B 1S0—Ph. 519-846-9885
Goslings in White Chinese and Embden.

Puerto Rico

Aibonito Hatchery, Inc., Ruto 2, Buzon 490, Aibonito, PR 00609—Ph. 809-735-8585
Goslings in Embden and Toulouse.

APPENDIX I

Sources of Supplies and Equipment

Complete Inventory

Burkey Co.
P.O. Box 29465
San Antonio, TX 78229
Ph. 512-696-0706

Canadian Poultry Supplies
Rt. 2
Lindsay, Ontario
Canada K9V 4R2

College Poultry Supplies
287 College St.
Toronto, Ontario
Canada M5T 1S2
Ph. 416-924-5598

Foy's Supplies
Box 27166
Golden Valley, MN 55427

Gragne Bros. Supplies
2883 Woodland Circle
Allison Park, PA 15101
Ph. 412-443-2486

Marsh Manufacturing, Inc.
14232 Brookhurst St.
Garden Grove, CA 92643
Ph. 714-534-6580

Northwest Farms, Inc.
P.O. Box 3003
Portland, OR 97208
Ph. 503-653-0344

Rocky Top Poultry Supply
P.O. Box 1006
Harriman, TN 37748
Ph. 615-882-8867

Ronson Farms
P.O. Box 12565
Columbus, OH 43212
Ph. 614-486-6219

Sidney Shoemaker Poultry Supplies
3091 Lincoln-Gilead Twp. Rd. 124
Rt. 3
Cardington, OH 43315
Ph. 419-864-6666

Stocklin Supply Co.
738 S.E. Lincoln
Portland, OR 98124
Ph. 503-234-0897

Strecker's Poultry Supply
Rt. 3, Box 365-K
Arroyo Grande, CA 93420

Stromberg's
50 Lakes Route
Pine River, MN 56474
Ph. 218-543-4223

Valentine Equipment Co.
9706 S. Industrial Drive
Bridgeview, IL 60455
Ph. 312-599-1101

Picking Wax and Equipment

Pickwick Co.
1120 Glass Road N.E.
Cedar Rapids, IA 52402
Ph. 319-393-7443

Incubators and
Brooding Equipment Only

Brower Manufacturing Co.
Box 5722
Quincy, IL 62301

Hockman's
12659 Devonshire
San Diego, CA 92107
Ph. 714-222-6983

Leahy Manufacturing Co.
406 W. 22 St.
Higginsville, MO 64037
Ph. 816-584-2641

The Humidaire Incubator Co.
217 W. Wyne St.
New Madison, OH 45346
Ph. 513-996-3001

Oak Ridge Manufacturing Co.
Veyo, UT 84778
Ph. 801-673-9190

Superior Incubator Co.
4734 Sanford
Houston, TX 77035
Ph. 713-729-2109

APPENDIX J

Suggested Reading

Magazines and Newspapers

Backyard Poultry, Rt. 1, Box 7, Waterloo, Wisconsin 53594. $7 yearly. Monthly magazine with articles geared for the small flock owner. Occasional information on geese.

Countryside, Jerome D. Belanger, editor and publisher, Rt. 1, Waterloo, Wisconsin 53594. $12 yearly. Authoritative monthly magazine for small farmers. Regular features on poultry with question and answer department.

Duck, Goose and Swan Magazine, Todd Miles, editor and publisher, Greystones Farm, Millbury, Massachusetts 01527. $8 yearly (6 issues), $1 for sample. New bimonthly magazine for anyone interested in raising and breeding waterfowl.

Feather Fancier, Corey R. Herrington, editor and publisher, P.O. Box 239, Erin, Ontario, Canada N0B 1T0. $6 yearly, 50¢ for sample. Monthly paper devoted to standard-bred poultry, pigeons and pet stock. Good source for addresses of Canadian poultry breeders and hatcheries.

Poultry Press, Robert F. DeLancey, editor and publisher, Box 947, York, Pennsylvania 17405. $5 yearly, 50¢ for sample. Monthly paper with articles on poultry shows, club news, and breeding and management tips. Good source for addresses of waterfowl breeders and hatcheries throughout North America.

Books

Light Weight Camping Equipment and How to Make It, by Gerry Cunningham and Margaret Hansson. Available from Gerry Division of Outdoor Sports Industries, 5450 North Valley Hwy, Denver, Colorado 80216. Gives patterns and instructions for making down-filled clothing.

Nutrient Requirements of Poultry, 7th revised edition (1977), National Academy of Sciences, 2101 Constitution Avenue, Washington, D.C. 20418. An informative though brief manual on poultry nutrition. Highly recommended for persons who desire a working understanding of poultry nutrition and who plan to formulate rations.

Poultry Nutrition Handbook, by Dr. John D. Summers and Dr. Steven Leeson. Available from Department of Animal and Poultry Science, Ontario Agriculture College, University of Guelph, Guelph, Ontario, Canada. $5. Contains extensive information on feeding requirements and ration formulas for all types of poultry.

Modern Waterfowl Management and Breeding Guide, by Oscar Grow. Available from American Bantam Association, P.O. Box 610, N. Amherst, Massachusetts 01059. $12. Contains detailed information on the origin, history and breeding of most breeds and species of domestic and semidomestic ducks, geese and swans. 359 pages, numerous illustrations, hardback.

Successful Duck & Goose Raising, by Darrel Sheraw. Available from Stromberg Publishing Co., Pine River, Minnesota 56474. $5.95. Most comprehensive book available on selecting and mating standard-bred waterfowl. 208 pages, 225 pictures, paperback.

Standard of Perfection for Domesticated Land Fowl and Water Fowl, American Poultry Association, Inc., Box 70, Cushing, Oklahoma 74023. $12. Describes in detail all varieties of large chickens, bantams, turkeys, ducks and geese recognized by the American Poultry Association. Of special interest for persons who raise purebred poultry. 600 pages, over 200 illustrations, hardback.

APPENDIX K

Organizations

International Waterfowl Breeders Association, Lyle Jones, Secy., 12402 Curtis Rd., Grass Lake, MI 49240. Dues $3. Sponsors meets at shows and sends out newsletters (2-4 pages).

International Toulouse Society, James Konecny, Secy., R. Oak Valley, Hampshire, IL 60140. Dues $5. Sends out a quarterly newsletter and sponsors meets at shows.

Eastern Waterfowl Breeders Association, Ray Jenkinson, Secy., Rt. 3, Box 39B, Stewartstown, PA 17363. Dues $5. Sends out a newsletter, sponsors an annual fall show and gives special awards.

American Poultry Association, Inc., Bertha Traver, Secy.-Treas., Rt. 4, Box 351, Troy, NY 12180. Dues $4. For breeders of all poultry. Membership includes newsletter and yearbook (112 pages in 1977) containing articles and advertisements from leading poultry breeders.

Society for Preservation of Poultry Antiquities, James K. Rice, Secy.-Treas., Rt. 3, Greenwood, WI 54437. Dues $5. Members receive S.P.A.A. Breeder Directory (last issue contained 116 pages and listed 329 poultry breeders throughout North America) and quarterly newsletters (6-12 pages) with information on all types of rare poultry.

Bibliography

Aitten, J.R. and Merritt, E.S., *Raising Geese*, Publication 848, Canada Department of Agriculture, Ottawa, Ontario, Canada, 1977.

American Poultry Association, Inc., *The American Standard of Perfection*, Cushing, Oklahoma, 1973.

Bernsohn, Ken, "Producing Your Own Down," *Organic Gardening and Farming*, Vol. 25, No. 3 (March 1978), p. 114.

Chatterton, F.J.S., *Ducks and Geese and How to Keep Them*, London, 1924.

Grow, Oscar, *Modern Waterfowl Management and Breeding Guide*, American Bantam Association, 1972.

Holderread, Dave, *The Home Duck Flock*, The Hen House, Corvallis, Oregon, 1978.

Ives, Paul, *Domestic Geese and Ducks*, Orange Judd Publishing Co., Inc., New York, 1947.

Kortright, Francis H., *The Ducks, Geese and Swans of North America*, The Stackpole Co., Harrisburg, Pennsylvania, and Wildlife Management Institute, Washington, D.C., 1976.

Leeson, Steven and Summers, John D., *Poultry Nutrition Handbook*, Department of Animal and Poultry Science, Ontario Agricultural College, University of Guelph, Guelph, Ontario, Canada.

Leonard, Dave, *Poultry Feeds and Feeding*, A guide for Peace Corps Volunteers (Mimeographed), Peace Corps Training Center, Arecibo, Puerto Rico, January 1968.

Lorenz, Konrad, *The Year of the Greylag Goose*, R. Piper & Co. Velag, 1979.

May, C.G., ed., *British Poultry Standard*, Poultry World and The Poultry Club of Great Britain, 1971.

Miller, William C. and West, Geoffry P., *Encyclopedia of Animal Care*, 9th ed., The Williams and Wilkins Co., Baltimore, Maryland, 1970.

National Research Council, *Nutrient Requirements of Poultry*, 7th revised ed., National Academy of Sciences, Washington, D.C., 1977.

Orr, H.L., *Duck and Goose Raising*, Publication 532, Department of Animal and Poultry Science, Ontario Agricultural College, University of Guelph, Guelph, Ontario, Canada.

Penionzhkevich, E.E., ed., *Poultry, Science and Practice*, Vol. I, Biology, Breeds and Breeding; Vol. II, Farming and Production. Translated from Russian. Published pursuant to agreement with U.S. Department of Agriculture and the National Science Foundation, Washington, D.C., 1968.

"Predator Problems," *Poultry Press*, Vol. 63, No. 9 (August 1977), p. 10.

"Predator Season's Here," *Poultry Press*, Vol. 63, No. 1 (December 1976), p. 1.

Robinson, John H., *The Growing of Ducks and Geese for Profit and Pleasure*, Reliable Poultry Journal Publishing Co., Dayton, Ohio, 1924.

Salsbury Laboratories, *Salsbury Manual of Poultry Diseases*, Charles City, Iowa, 1971.

Schaible, Philip J., *Poultry: Feeds and Nutrition*, Avi Publishing Co., Inc., 1970.

Sheraw, Darrel, *Successful Duck and Goose Raising*, Stromberg Publishing Co., Pine River, Minnesota, 1975.

Siegmund, O.H., ed., *The Merck Veterinary Manual*, 4th ed., Merck & Co., Inc., Rahway, New Jersey, 1975.

Stoddard, H.H., *Domestic Waterfowl*, Hartford, Connecticut, 1885.

Strond, Robert, *Strond's Digest on the Diseases of Birds*, T.F.H. Publication, Inc., 1964.

Tegetmeier, W.G., *The Poultry Book*, 1873.

Turk, D.E. and Barnett, B.D., *Cholesterol Content of Market Eggs*, Poultry Science Journal, Vol. 50, No. 5, (September 1971), pp. 1303-1306.

United States Department of Agriculture, *Raising Geese*, Farmer's Bulletin, No. 2251, 1972.

Watt, Bernice K. and Merrill, Annabel L., for the U.S. Department of Agriculture, *Handbook of Nutritional Contents of Foods*, Dover Publications, Inc., New York, 1975.

Glossary

AIR CELL — A stationary air pocket that normally develops between the two shell membranes in the large end of eggs soon after they are laid. As the contents of an egg dehydrate in storage or during incubation, the air cell increases in volume.

ALBUMEN — The egg-white.

BIOTIN — A B-complex vitamin that can be rendered unavailable if raw eggs are fed to poultry. (See Appendix B for symptoms of a deficiency.)

BLOW-OUT — This term is used to describe both rotting eggs that explode during incubation or female birds that expel their oviduct while attempting to lay an egg.

BREED — A subdivision of the goose family whose members possess similar body size and temperaments and the ability to pass these characteristics on to their offspring.

BREEDER RATION — Feed that is used during the breeding season and formulated to stimulate good egg production, fertility and hatchability.

BREEDING STOCK — Selected adult geese used to produce goslings.

BROODINESS — The maternal instinct that causes a goose to want to incubate eggs.

COCCIDIOSTAT — A medication used to control the one-celled parasite coccidia.

CONCENTRATED FEED — Feeds that are high in protein, carbohydrates, fats, vitamins and minerals, and low in fiber.

CROSSBREED — The mating of male geese of one breed to females of another breed.

CULLING — The removal of inferior (crippled, deformed, diseased, low-producing) birds from the flock.

DEWLAP — A fold of feather-covered skin hanging from the throat and upper neck in some geese.

EGG TOOTH — A small, horny protuberance attached to the bean of the bills on newly hatched birds that is used to help break the shell at hatching time. Normally falls off several days after the bird hatches.

EMBRYO — A bird before it emerges from the egg.

ESOPHAGUS — The tube in which food passes from the mouth to the digestive tract. (Geese do not have true crops.)

FEED CONVERSION — The ability of birds to convert feed into body growth or eggs. To calculate feed conversion ratios, divide pounds of feed consumed by pounds of body weight or eggs.

FERTILITY — In reference to eggs, the capability of producing an embryo. Fertility is expressed as a percentage that equals the total number of eggs set minus those that are infertile, divided by the total number set, times 100.

FLIGHTS — The large feathers of the wings, including the primaries and secondaries.

FULL-FEATHERED — When a bird has a complete set of feathers.

GANDER — The male goose.

GIZZARD — The muscular organ that grinds the food eaten by birds.

GOOSE — In general, any member of the subfamily Anserinae. It is often used specifically in reference to female geese.

GOSLINGS — Young geese up until feathers have completely replaced their baby down.

GROWING RATION — Feed that is formulated to stimulate fast growth.

HATCHABILITY — The ability of eggs to hatch. Hatchability can be expressed as (1) a percentage of the fertile eggs set (total number of goslings hatched divided by the number of fertile eggs set, times 100) or (2) a percentage of all eggs set (total number of goslings hatched divided by the total number of eggs set, times 100).

INBRED — Offspring that are the result of mating closely related birds — such as brother to sister, father to daughter, son to mother.

KEEL — A pendulous fold of skin hanging from the underbody of geese.

KINKED NECK — A deformed neck with an obvious crook.

KNOB — A bulbous, fleshy projection on the forehead of African and Chinese geese.

LAMELLA — Tooth-like serrations on the inner edges and roof of the bill of geese.

LOBE — Either one or two folds of skin that hang from the abdomen of many domestic geese.

MAINTENANCE RATION — Feed used for adult geese during the off season when they are not breeding. (Also known as a holding ration.)

MOLT — The natural replacement of old feathers with new ones.

NIACIN — A B-complex vitamin (nicotinic acid) that geese require in larger quantities than chickens. A niacin deficiency causes stunted growth, poor feathering and crippled legs.

OIL GLAND — Also known as oil sac or uropygial gland, this gland produces an oily feather conditioner and water repellent that is spread onto the plumage as the bird preens.

OVIDUCT — The elongated gland where eggs are formed.

PIN FEATHERS — New feathers that are just emerging from the skin.

PIP — The first visible break hatching goslings make in the egg shell.

POST MORTEM -- The examination of a dead bird to determine the cause of death.

PRODUCTION-BRED — Geese that have been selected for top meat and/or egg production.

PUREBRED — Geese of a specific breed that have not been crossed with other breeds for many generations.

RELATIVE HUMIDITY — The ratio of the quantity of water vapor in the air to the greatest amount possible at a given temperature. Therefore, 100% relative humidity is total saturation, while 0% would indicate the complete absence of moisture.

ROACH BACK — A malformed spinal column that causes the back to be shortened and humped.

SHELL MEMBRANES — Two pliable membranes that line the interior of the egg shell.

SLIPPED WING — A deformed wing that does not fold smoothly against the bird's body.

STRAIN — A family or line of livestock that has been selected for specific characteristics over several generations by a breeder.

STANDARD-BRED — Geese that have been stringently selected over many generations according to the ideal that is set forth in the Standard of Perfection.

STANDARD OF PERFECTION — A book containing pictures and descriptions of the physical characteristics desired in the perfect bird of each recognized breed and variety of poultry.

STARTING RATION — A high protein feed used the first couple weeks to get goslings off to a good start.

STRAIGHT RUN — Young poultry that have not been sexed.

TRACHEA — The flexible windpipe that allows passage of air from the bird's larynx to the bronchi and lungs.

VARIETY — A subdivision of the breeds. In geese, the varieties within a breed are identified by their plumage color.

VENT — The external opening of both the digestive tract and the oviduct.

WATERFOWL — Birds that naturally spend most of their lives on and near water. This term is often used in specific reference to ducks, geese and swans.

WET-BULB THERMOMETER — A mercury thermometer that has a tubular wick, with one end fitted over the thermometer's bulb and the other end inserted into a container of water. This instrument is used to measure the relative humidity in the incubator.

WRY TAIL — A deformity that causes the tail to be constantly cocked to one side.

Index

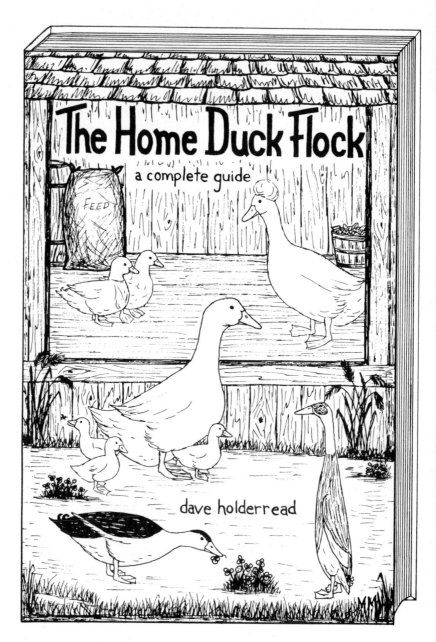

a complete guide to raising

The Home Duck Flock

by Dave Holderread

If you've ever wished for comprehensive information on raising ducks, this book was prepared for you. In plain language, *The Home Duck Flock* provides all the know-how you'll need to start a duck flock and achieve the highest production and enjoyment from your birds, while avoiding unneeded disappointments.

Within its 200 pages you'll find . . .

- eleven informative chapters covering the advantages of ducks, their limitations, external characteristics, behavior, the breeds, acquiring stock, incubation, rearing ducklings, managing adult ducks, health and physical problems and their treatment, and butchering

- 100 photos and drawings enlivening and clarifying the text

- instructions on managing for top egg and meat production, sexing day-old and adult birds, making down filled clothing, preventing losses to predators, identifying and curing vitamin and mineral deficiencies, and handling aggressive birds

- twenty easy-to-use feed rations formulated specifically for ducks, plus instructions on how to devise rations utilizing locally available ingredients

- a directory to sixty of North America's leading breeders and hatcheries and twenty sources for supplies and equipment

- descriptions and photographs of sixteen common and rare breeds — Pekin, Rouen, Muscovy, Campbell, Runner, Cayuga, Crested, Swedish, Orpington, Call, East Indie, Mallard, Bali, Magpie and Australian Spotted

- zesty recipes

. . . and much more. This is a book you'll find yourself coming back to time and again, and with its convenient reference format, you will be able to locate information quickly.

Hen House Publications
P.O. Box 492
Corvallis, Oregon 97330

Paperback $ 6.60 postpaid
Hardback   10.60 postpaid